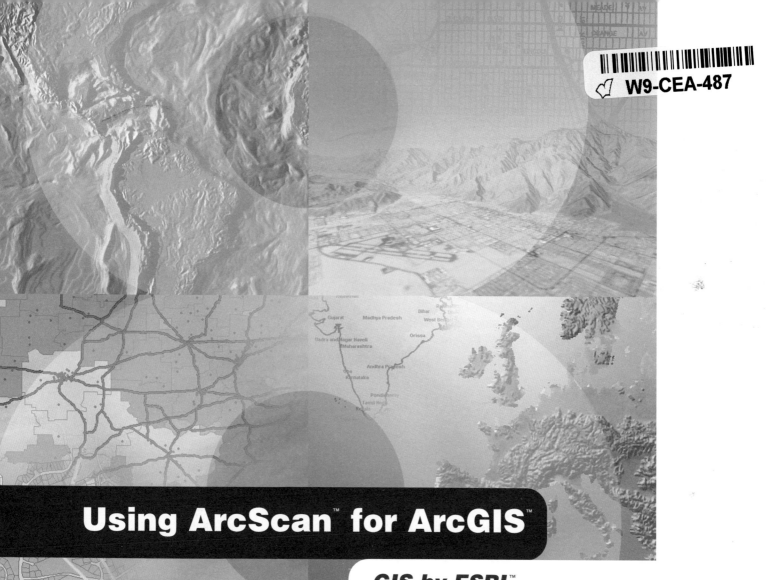

Using ArcScan™ for ArcGIS™

GIS by ESRI™

WRITER

Phil Sanchez

Important ArcScan for ArcGIS Information

ESRI® ArcScan for ArcGIS™ is available for ArcView® as well as ArcEditor™ and ArcInfo™. Please disregard any printed information to the contrary.

CRWN19M1/03sb
93150

Contents

5 Batch vectorization   87

Appendix   121

Glossary   125

Index   135

Introducing ArcScan

Welcome to ESRI® ArcScan™ for ArcGIS™, the raster-to-vector conversion extension to ArcMap™ available with the ArcInfo™ and ArcEditor™ licenses. The ArcScan extension allows you to take scanned images of maps and convert them into vector-based feature layers, such as shapefiles and geodatabase feature classes. Vectorization can be performed manually by interactively tracing raster cells or automatically using the batch mode.

The process of converting raster data into vector features relies on user-defined settings. These settings allow you to influence the geometric composition of the output vector features. Once you have determined the optimal vectorization settings for your data, they can be readily saved and reused.

The ArcScan extension also provides tools that allow you to perform simple raster editing to prepare your raster layers for vectorization. This practice, known as *raster preprocessing*, can help you eliminate unwanted raster elements that are not in the scope of your vectorization projects.

Chapter 1 presents an overview of the ArcScan functionality. Chapter 2 contains a quick-start tutorial to help you get up to speed with the common ArcScan functionality. Chapter 3 discusses how to set up the ArcScan environment. Chapter 4 describes raster snapping and tracing. Chapter 5 explains raster preprocessing and batch vectorization.

What can you do with the ArcScan extension?

ArcScan provides tools that allow you to convert scanned images into vector-based feature layers. ArcScan also supports the ability to select and edit raster cells to help you refine the image you are working with. When combined, these tools extend ArcMap software by providing new techniques for integrating features derived from raster imagery into your geographic information system (GIS).

Raster display of contour lines; centerline vectorization of contour lines

Batch vectorization requires settings that influence how the output vector features are generated. These settings, also known as *styles*, can be saved and reused with raster images that possess similar characteristics.

A typical scanned parcel map from an engineering department

Batch vectorization

One of the key features of the ArcScan extension is its ability to automatically convert raster data into vector features. This process, known as *batch vectorization*, can significantly reduce the time it takes to vectorize scanned images.

ArcScan supports two types of vectorization methods: centerline and outline. Depending on your requirements and the type of scanned images you are working with, the vectorization method you employ will vary.

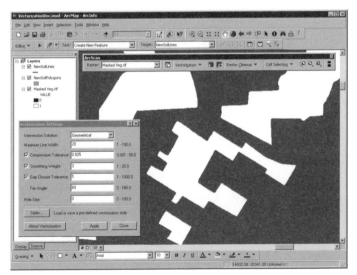

The vectorization settings dialog box and preview display in ArcMap

Interactive vectorization

Along with batch vectorization, you can also generate features manually. This process is known as *interactive vectorization* and is similar to the existing techniques used to create features with the Editor. Interactive vectorization consists of two components: raster snapping and raster tracing.

Raster snapping

The ArcScan extension supports the ability to snap to raster cells. Although not required for raster tracing, raster snapping can help ensure that you create features accurately. You can snap to raster centerlines, intersections, corners, ends, and solids.

Snapping to raster intersections (left); snapping to raster centerlines (right)

You can specify your raster snapping preferences using the Editor's Snapping Environment dialog box.

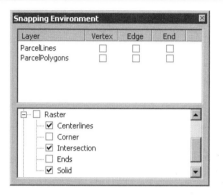

Raster snapping properties

Raster tracing

Raster tracing is useful in cases in which you need to have more control over the vectorization process or need to vectorize a small portion of an image. The Vectorization trace tool allows you to manually trace raster cells and generate features for raster data that you wish to vectorize.

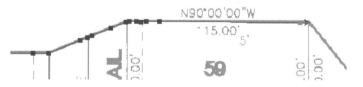

Centerline tracing used to create line features

With the Vectorization Trace tool, you simply point the cursor in the direction you wish to vectorize and click. With each click, features will be generated at the centerline of the raster cells. The current vectorization settings will influence the output vector geometry. You have the option to generate line or polygon features.

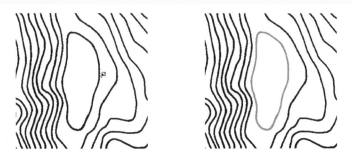

Raster display of contour lines (left); selected series of connected cells (right)

The Select connected cells dialog box allows you to perform complex cell selection based on pixel area and envelope extents.

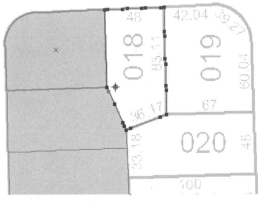

Raster snapping and tracing used to create polygon features

Raster selection

ArcScan supports tools for selecting raster cells. You can create raster selections interactively by clicking a series of connected cells or by executing an expression-based query. These selection tools can help you define the scope of your vectorization.

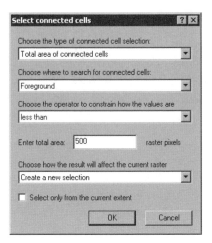

Select connected cells dialog box

Raster image prior to selection (left); cell selection based on pixel area (right)

This can help you filter which cells you wish to omit from or include in the vectorization.

Simple raster editing

ArcScan also supports tools for editing raster images. You can draw, fill, and erase raster cells all within an ArcMap edit session. These steps, known as *raster cleanup*, allow you to eliminate raster cells that are not in the scope of the vectorization. Additionally, you can export the modified raster to a new file in case you need to preserve the original copy.

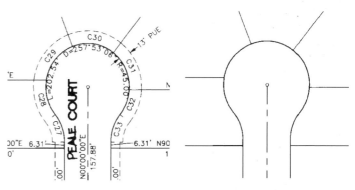

Image prior to and after cleanup

Tips on learning how to use ArcScan

If you're new to GIS, take some time to familiarize yourself with ArcMap and ArcCatalog™. The books *Using ArcMap* and *Using ArcCatalog* contain tutorials to show you how to make maps and manage GIS data.

Begin learning to use the ArcScan extension in Chapter 2, 'Quick-start tutorial'. In Chapter 2 you'll learn how to snap to raster cells, trace raster cells, select raster cells, perform simple raster editing, and batch vectorize. The ArcScan extension comes with the data used in this tutorial, so you can follow along step by step at your computer. You can also read the tutorial without using your computer.

Finding answers to questions

Like most people, your goal is to complete your task while investing a minimum amount of time and effort in learning how to use the software. You want intuitive, easy-to-use software that gives you immediate results without having to read pages and pages of documentation. However, when you do have a question, you want the answer quickly so that you can complete your task. That's what this book is all about—getting you the answers you need when you need them.

This book describes how to use ArcScan to perform interactive and batch vectorization. Although you can read this book from start to finish, you'll likely use it more as a reference. When you want to know how to do a particular task, such as tracing raster cells, just look it up in the table of contents or the index. You'll find a concise, step-by-step description of how to complete the task. Some chapters also include detailed information that you can read if you want to learn more about the concepts behind the tasks. You can also refer to the glossary in this book if you come across any unfamiliar terms.

Getting help on your computer

In addition to this book, use the ArcGIS online Help system to learn how to use ArcScan. To learn how to use Help, see the *Using ArcMap* book.

Contacting ESRI

If you need to contact ESRI for technical support, see the product registration and support card you received with ArcScan for ArcGIS or refer to 'Contacting Technical Support' in the 'Getting more help' section of the ArcGIS Desktop Help system. You can also visit ESRI on the Web at *www.esri.com* and *support.esri.com* for more information on ArcScan and ArcGIS.

ESRI education solutions

ESRI provides educational opportunities related to geographic information science, GIS applications, and technology. You can choose among instructor-led courses, Web-based courses, and self-study workbooks to find educational solutions that fit your learning style. For more information go to *www.esri.com/education.*

Quick-start tutorial

IN THIS CHAPTER

- **Exercise 1: Raster tracing**

- **Exercise 2: Batch vectorization**

ArcScan for ArcGIS software has the tools you need to convert your scanned raster images into vector-based GIS layers. This process can be performed interactively or in an automated fashion.

The easiest way to learn how to use ArcScan is to complete the exercises in this tutorial.

Exercise 1 shows you how to set up the raster snapping options and environment, snap to raster cells, and trace raster cells to create line and polygon features.

Exercise 2 teaches you how to edit a raster layer to remove unwanted cells, apply vectorization settings, preview the vectorization, and generate features using the batch vectorization mode.

Each of these exercises takes between 15 and 20 minutes to complete. You have the option of working through the entire tutorial or completing each exercise one at a time.

Exercise 1: Raster tracing

ArcScan makes it easy to create new features from scanned raster images. This process can significantly reduce the time it takes for you to incorporate raster data into your vector database.

In this exercise, you will generate features from a scanned parcel map by interactively tracing raster cells. You will begin by starting ArcMap and loading a map document that contains the raster dataset and two shapefiles.

Starting ArcMap

Before you can complete the tasks in this tutorial, you must start ArcMap and load the tutorial data.

1. Double-click a shortcut installed on your desktop or use the Programs list in your Start menu to start ArcMap.

2. Click the Open button on the Standard toolbar.

3. Navigate to the ArcScanTrace.mxd map document in the ArcScan directory where you installed the tutorial data and select it (C:\ArcGIS\ArcTutor is the default location).

4. Click Open.

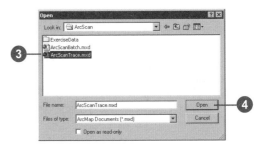

Changing the raster layer symbology

Raster layers must be symbolized as bi-level images to use the ArcScan tools and commands. You will change the raster symbology from stretched to unique values.

1. Right-click the ParcelScan.img raster layer in the ArcMap Table of Contents and click Properties from the context menu to display the Layer Properties dialog box.

2. Click the Symbology tab on the Layer Properties dialog box.

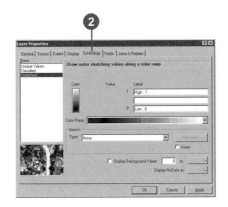

3. In the Show box, click the Unique Values display option.

4. Click OK.

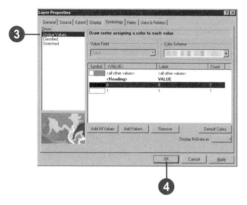

Locating the trace area

Spatial bookmarks are named extents that can be saved in map documents. Creating a bookmark for areas that you visit frequently will save you time. For information on how to create and manage spatial bookmarks, see *Using ArcMap*.

You will now zoom to a spatial bookmark created for this exercise.

1. Click the View menu, point to Bookmarks, and click Trace lines to set the current view to the edit area of the exercise.

When the display refreshes, you should see the trace area.

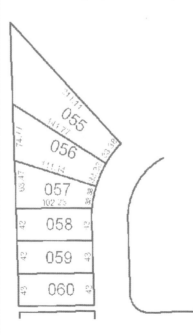

Start editing

The ArcScan extension is only active in an edit session. The Start Editing command enables you to begin an edit session.

1. Click the Editor menu and click Start Editing to begin the edit session.

Setting the raster snapping options

Raster snapping requires settings that influence the behavior of the tracing. These options are set in the Raster Snapping Options dialog box.

1. Click the Raster Snapping Options button on the ArcScan toolbar to open the Raster Snapping dialog box.

2. Set the maximum line width value to 7. This setting will ensure that you are able to snap to raster cells that represent the lot boundaries.

3. Click OK.

4. Click the Editor menu and click Snapping to open the Snapping Environment dialog box.

5. Click the plus sign next to Raster to expand it.

6. Check the Centerlines and Intersection options for raster snapping.

Creating line features by tracing raster cells

Now that you have set up your raster snapping environment, you are ready to begin tracing the raster cells. You will use the Vectorization Trace tool for this step.

1. Click the Vectorization Trace button on the ArcScan toolbar.

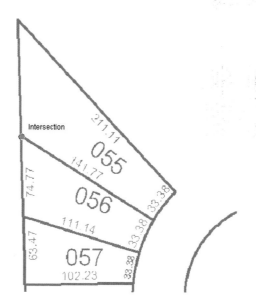

2. Move the pointer until it snaps to the intersection of the lot boundaries and click to start tracing.

3. Point the Vectorization Trace tool downward and click to start creating the line feature.

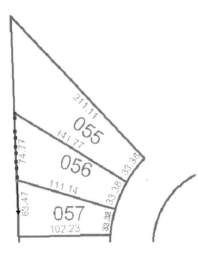

4. Continue to point and click with the Vectorization Trace tool to trace the exterior boundary of the lots.

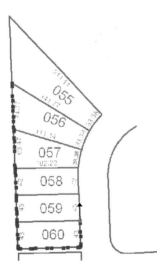

5. Once you have finished tracing around the lot boundaries, press F2 to finish the sketch.

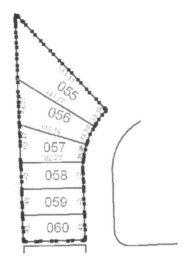

A line feature now represents the exterior boundaries of the scanned parcel lots.

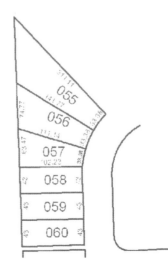

Creating polygon features by tracing raster cells

Now that you have successfully traced raster cells to create line features, you will create polygon features using the Vectorization Trace tool.

1. To get a better view of the area that will be traced, you need to zoom to the bookmarked extent called Trace polygons. Click the View menu, point to Bookmarks, and click Trace polygons.

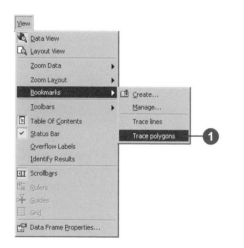

Changing the edit target layer

You must change the edit target layer from ParcelLines to ParcelPolygons to create polygon features when tracing.

1. Click the Target dropdown box on the Editor toolbar and choose ParcelPolygons.

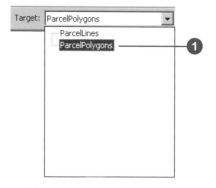

2. Click the Vectorization Trace button on the ArcScan toolbar.

3. Move the pointer until it snaps to the lower-left corner of lot 061 and click to start tracing.

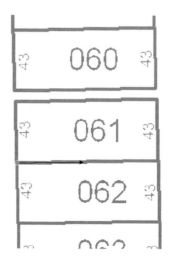

4. Point the arrow toward the lower-right corner of the lot and click to start creating the segments of the polygon feature.

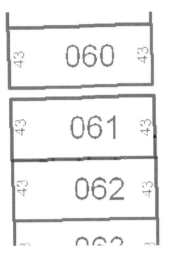

5. Continue to trace the lot boundary in a counterclockwise direction.

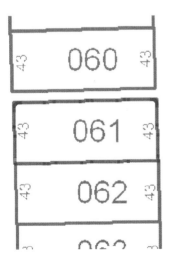

6. When the cursor has returned to the starting point of the trace, press F2 to complete the polygon.

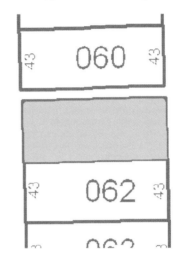

Finishing your edit session

Once you have finished tracing the raster cells and have disabled the Vectorization Trace tool, you can stop editing and complete the exercise by saving your edits.

1. Click the Editor menu and click Stop Editing.

2. Click Yes to save your edits.

In this exercise you learned how to set the raster snapping options and environment, snap to raster cells, and trace raster cells to create new line and polygon features. These steps covered the main components of the raster tracing process. The next exercise will show you how to edit a raster layer and automatically generate features for an entire raster layer using the batch vectorization tools.

Exercise 2: Batch vectorization

In this exercise, you will edit a scanned parcel map to remove cells from the raster that are not in the scope of the vectorization. Once the raster has been cleaned up, you will generate features using the batch vectorization mode. You will begin by starting ArcMap and loading a map document that contains the raster dataset and two shapefiles.

Starting ArcMap and beginning editing

Before you can complete the tasks in this tutorial, you must start ArcMap and load the tutorial data.

1. Double-click a shortcut installed on your desktop or use the Programs list in your Start menu to start ArcMap.

2. Click the Open button on the Standard toolbar.

3. Navigate to the ArcScanBatch.mxd map document in the ArcScan directory where you installed the tutorial data and select it (C:\ArcGIS\ArcTutor is the default location).

4. Click Open.

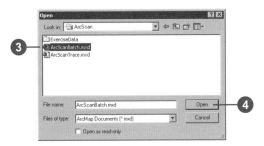

Changing the raster layer symbology

Raster layers must be symbolized as bi-level images to use the ArcScan tools and commands. You will change the raster symbology from stretched to unique values.

1. Right-click the ParcelScan.img raster layer in the ArcMap Table of Contents and click Properties from the context menu to display the Layer Properties dialog box.

2. Click the Symbology tab on the Layer Properties dialog box.

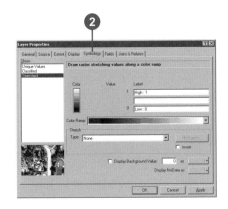

3. In the Show box, click the Unique Values display option.

4. Click OK.

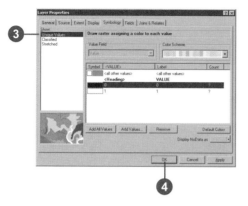

Locating the cleanup area

Spatial bookmarks are named extents that can be saved in map documents. Creating a bookmark for areas that you visit frequently will save you time. For information on how to create and manage spatial bookmarks, see *Using ArcMap*.

You will now zoom to a spatial bookmark created for this exercise.

1. Click the View menu, point to Bookmarks, and click Raster cleanup to set the current view to the edit area of the exercise.

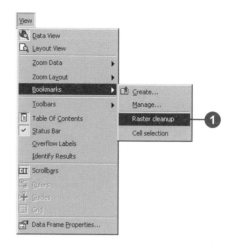

When the display refreshes, you should see the edit area.

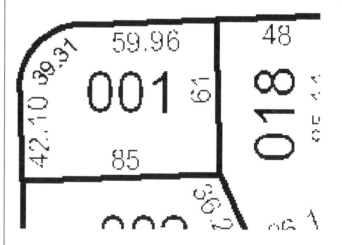

Start editing

The ArcScan extension is only active in an edit session. The Start Editing command enables you to begin an edit session.

1. Click the Editor menu and click Start Editing to begin the edit session.

Cleaning up the raster for vectorization

When performing batch vectorization, it is sometimes necessary to edit the raster image prior to generating features. This process is referred to as *raster cleanup* and involves the removal of unwanted cells from the raster image that are not in the scope of the vectorization. ArcScan provides the tools to perform raster cleanup.

You will now use the Raster Cleanup tools to remove unwanted text from the ParcelScan image.

1. Click the Raster Cleanup menu and click Start Cleanup to start the raster cleanup session.

2. Click the Raster Cleanup menu and click Raster Painting Toolbar to display the Raster Painting Toolbar.

3. Click the Erase tool located on the Raster Painting toolbar.

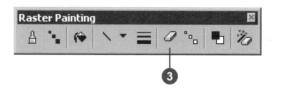

4. Click and hold down the left mouse key and erase the text located at the top of the parcel lot.

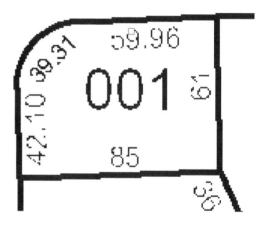

5. Continue to erase the text with the Erase tool until it has been completely removed from the image.

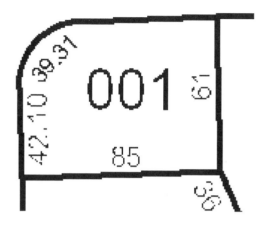

In addition to the Erase tool, the Raster Painting toolbar supports another tool designed to erase cells. This tool is called the Magic Erase tool, and it allows you to erase a series of connected cells by simply clicking or dragging a box around them.

6. Click the Magic Erase tool located on the Raster Painting toolbar.

7. Drag a box around the text located in the center of the parcel lot to remove it.

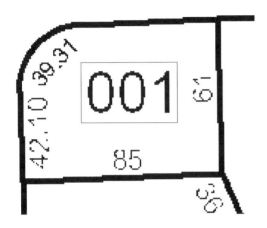

The text is now removed from the raster.

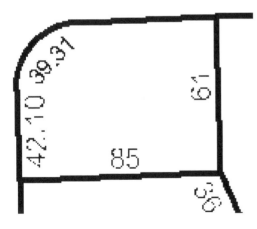

Using the cell selection tools to assist with raster cleanup

In the previous steps, you learned how to use the Erase and Magic Erase tools to remove unwanted cells from the raster image. However, if the image you are working with requires much cleanup, these techniques could be time consuming. To help streamline this process, you can use the cell selection tools in conjunction with the raster cleanup tools.

1. To get a better view of the edit area, you need to zoom to the bookmarked extent called Cell selection. Click the View menu, point to Bookmarks, and click Cell selection.

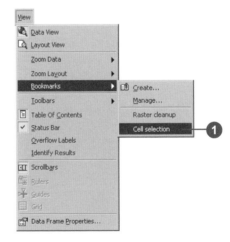

When the display refreshes, you should see the edit area.

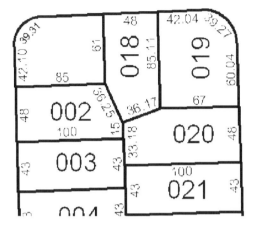

2. Click the Cell Selection menu and click Select Connected Cells.

3. In the Select connected cells dialog box, enter a value of 500 for the total area of raster pixels. This expression will select all the cells that represent text in the raster.

4. Click OK.

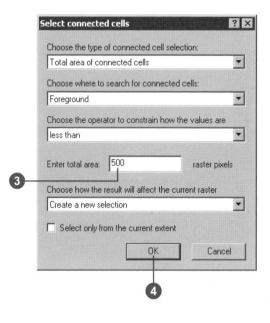

The cells that represent the text in the raster are now selected.

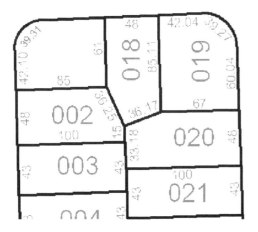

5. Click the Raster Cleanup menu and click Erase Selected Cells to delete the selected cells.

The selected cells are now erased.

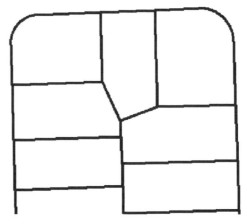

Using the vectorization settings

Batch vectorization relies on user-defined settings. These settings influence the geometry of the generated features. These settings may vary depending on the type of raster data you are working with. Once you have determined the appropriate settings for your raster, you can save them within the map document or to a separate file. You will use the Vectorization Settings dialog box to apply the settings.

1. Click the Vectorization menu and click Vectorization Settings to open the Vectorization Settings dialog box.

You will now modify the vectorization settings to ensure optimal results when generating features.

2. Change the Maximum Line Width value to 10.

3. Change the Compression Tolerance value to 0.1.

4. Click Apply to update the settings.

5. Click Close.

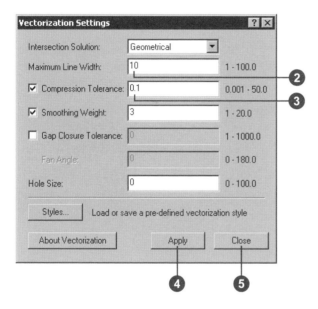

Previewing the vectorization

ArcScan provides a way to preview the batch vectorization prior to generating features. This can help you save time by allowing you to see how the settings will affect the vectorization. When the settings are changed, the preview can be updated by clicking the Apply button located on the Vectorization Settings dialog box. This design allows you to fine-tune the vectorization settings.

1. Click the Vectorization menu and click Show Preview.

The vectorization preview is displayed in the map.

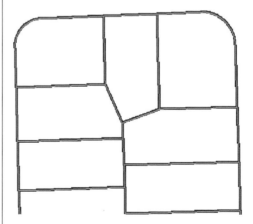

Generating features

The final step in the batch vectorization process is to generate features. The Generate Features dialog box allows you to select the vector layers that will store the new features and execute the vectorization.

1. Click the Vectorization menu and click Generate Features.

2. Choose the ParcelLinesBatch layer.

3. Click OK.

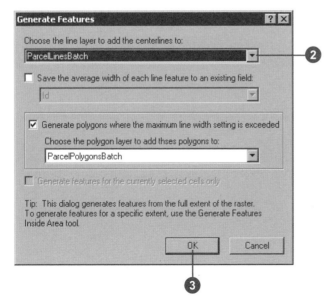

4. Right-click the ParcelScan.img raster layer in the ArcMap Table of Contents and click Zoom To Layer from the Context menu to view all of the new features that were generated.

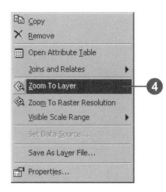

When the display refreshes, you should see the vector features that now represent the raster cells.

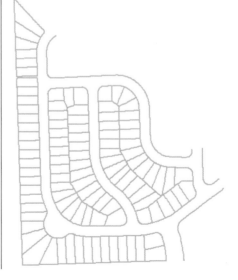

Finishing your edit session

Once you have finished generating features, you can stop editing and complete the exercise by saving your edits.

1. Click the Editor menu and click Stop Editing.

2. Click Yes to save your edits.

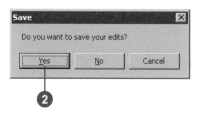

In this exercise you learned how to use the raster cleanup and cell selection tools to edit a raster layer, apply vectorization settings, preview the vectorization, and generate features. These steps covered the major components of the batch vectorization process.

This concludes the tutorial. You have been introduced to the most commonly used tools and commands for raster tracing and batch vectorization. The rest of this book will present additional information that will help you better understand the ArcScan extension.

ArcScan basics

IN THIS CHAPTER

- **Understanding a raster dataset**

- **Coordinate space and the raster dataset**

- **An overview of the ArcScan extension**

- **The ArcScan toolbar**

- **How ArcScan works in the editing environment**

- **Adding the Editor toolbar**

- **Starting and stopping an edit session**

- **Enabling the ArcScan extension**

- **Adding the ArcScan toolbar**

- **Changing the raster layer symbology**

- **Selecting the target raster layer and the vectorization options**

ArcScan converts raster data into vector-based feature layers in ArcMap. In addition, you can leverage the tools and commands available in the Editor toolbar to further refine this newly created data. ArcScan goes beyond the traditional methods of manual vectorization by introducing new tools to automate the raster selection and cleanup process. Whether you choose to trace raster cells interactively or batch vectorize an entire raster image, ArcScan provides an efficient way to integrate raster data into your GIS.

This chapter provides an overview of the raster datasets as well as an introduction on how to get started with ArcScan. It also describes how ArcScan works in conjunction with the Editor toolbar. Topics covered include enabling the ArcScan extension, adding the ArcScan toolbar, symbolizing raster data, and setting the vectorization options.

Understanding a raster dataset

Vector data—such as coverages and shapefiles—represents geographic features with lines, points, and polygons. Rasters—such as images and grids—represent geographic features by dividing the data into discrete squares called cells.

A raster can represent:

- Thematic data, such as land use, temperature, and elevation
- Spectral data, such as satellite images and aerial photographs
- Pictures, such as satellite images and aerial photographs

In ArcScan, you will work primarily with rasters that represent scanned maps and drawings. This section will provide a brief overview of raster data.

The cell

A raster dataset is made up of cells. Each *cell*, or pixel, is a square that represents a specific portion of an area. All cells in a raster must be the same size. The cells in a raster dataset can be any size that you desire, but they should be small enough to accomplish the most detailed analysis. A cell can represent a square kilometer, a square meter, or even a square centimeter.

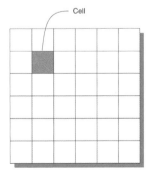

Rows and columns

Cells are arranged in rows and columns, an arrangement that produces a Cartesian matrix. The rows of the matrix are parallel to the x-axis of the Cartesian plane, and the columns are parallel to the y-axis. Each cell has a unique row and column address. All locations in a study site are covered by the matrix.

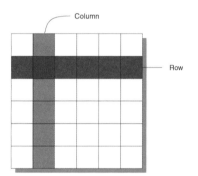

Values

Each cell is assigned a specific value to identify or describe the class, category, or group that the cell belongs to or the magnitude or quantity of the phenomenon that the raster describes. The characteristics the values represent include soil type, soil texture, land use class, water body type, road class, and housing type.

A value can also represent the magnitude, distance, or relationship of the cell on a continuous surface. Elevation, slope, aspect, noise pollution from an airport, and pH concentration from a bog are all examples of continuous surfaces.

For rasters representing images and photographs, the values can represent colors or spectral reflectance.

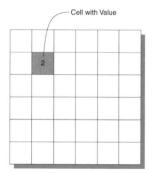

Cell with Value

Coordinate space and the raster dataset

Coordinate space defines the spatial relationship between the locations in a raster dataset. All raster datasets are in some coordinate space. This coordinate space may be a real-world coordinate system or image space. Since almost all raster datasets represent some real-world location, it is best to have that dataset in the real-world coordinate system that best represents it. Converting a raster dataset from a nonreal-world coordinate system—image space—to a real-world coordinate system is called *georeferencing*.

For a raster dataset, the orientation of the cells is determined by the x- and y-axes of the coordinate system. Cell boundaries are parallel to the x- and y-axis, and the cells are square in map coordinates. Cells are always referenced by an x,y location in map coordinate space and never by specifying a row–column location.

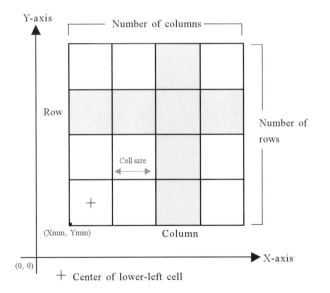

The x,y Cartesian coordinate system associated with a raster dataset that is in a real-world coordinate space is defined with respect to a *map projection*. Map projections transform the three-dimensional surface of the earth to allow the raster to be displayed and stored as a two-dimensional map.

The process of rectifying a raster dataset to map coordinates or converting a raster dataset from one projection to another is referred to as *geometric transformation*.

Georeferencing a raster dataset

To georeference a raster dataset from image space to a real-world coordinate system, you need to know the location of recognizable features in both coordinate spaces. These locations are used to create control points. The control points are used to build a polynomial transformation that will warp the image from one coordinate space to another. This can be done with the Georeferencing toolbar (click View, point to Toolbars, and click Georeferencing).

Control points are locations that can be accurately identified on the raster dataset and in real-world coordinates. These identifiable locations may be road and stream intersections, building corners, bridges, the mouth of a stream, rock outcrops, and identifiable points on geometric landscape features, such as the end of a jetty of land, the corner of an established field, or the intersection of two hedgerows.

For each control point selected on the input raster dataset, the output location may be specified either by graphically selecting a point that is already in the desired output coordinate system or by typing in the known output coordinates. The relationship between the control points chosen in the raster dataset and the output coordinate space is then determined.

Using this relationship and a polynomial transformation, the raster dataset is converted from nonreal-world space to real-world space.

For more information about georeferencing a raster dataset, please see the 'About georeferencing' topic in the ArcGIS Desktop Help system.

An overview of the ArcScan extension

The ArcScan extension provides tools and commands that support the conversion of raster data to vector features. This process, referred to as *vectorization*, can be performed interactively or in an automated fashion.

The interactive vectorization experience, referred to as *raster tracing*, requires that you trace the raster cells in the map to create vector features. The automated vectorization experience, referred to as *batch vectorization*, requires that you generate features for the entire raster based on settings that you specify.

ArcScan also supports tools to help with the preparation of raster data for vectorization. These include tools for selecting and editing raster cells to help you define the scope of the raster-to-vector conversion.

Who should use ArcScan?

Organizations that need to convert raster images into vector-based feature layers are the primary candidates for using the ArcScan extension. Since a large amount of geographic information still exists in the form of hard-copy maps, having a tool to integrate these documents into a GIS is crucial. These legacy documents may derive from engineering, survey, and cartographic professionals. ArcScan provides an efficient way to streamline this integration when compared to traditional techiques, such as digitizing.

How does ArcScan work in the ArcGIS environment?

The ArcScan toolset is an add-on component of the ArcGIS desktop suite. Licensed as a separate extension, ArcScan works within the ArcMap environment and relies on its own user interface, which supports the tools and commands used for the vectorization process. The ArcScan extension is designed to work with either the ArcEditor or ArcInfo licenses.

Getting started with ArcScan

As with other ArcGIS extensions, you must first enable the ArcScan extension in ArcMap before you can use it. ArcGIS will manage the licenses and will notify you if one is not available. You must also add the ArcScan toolbar to your map to access the tools and commands that support the vectorization work flow. Any map document that is saved with the ArcScan toolbar present will automatically retain the toolbar the next time the document is opened.

Since ArcScan is designed to work with the Editor, you must start an edit session to activate the toolbar. This requires that an editable shapefile or geodatabase feature class layer exists in the map. The tools and commands supported by the Editor can be used in conjunction with the ArcScan tools and commands. In addition, ArcScan will respect Editor settings, such as the snapping environment, current edit tasks, and target feature layers.

Symbolizing raster layers for ArcScan

ArcScan can vectorize any raster format supported by ArcGIS so long as it is represented as a bi-level image. This requires that you symbolize raster layers with two unique colors. You can use the ArcMap unique value or classify rendering option to separate the raster into two colors. Most scanned documents tend to consist of two colors that delineate the foreground and background values. Typically, the foreground is represented as a dark color, such as black, and the background is represented as a light color, such as white. However, these colors can be reversed or represented by different values. As long as the two colors possess unique values, ArcScan will support vectorization for the current foreground raster cells.

Selecting connected cells

ArcScan supports the ability to select connected raster cells. Connected raster cells are raster pixels that share contiguous borders. This can be either in a side-by-side or diagonal arrangement. This functionality allows you to select portions of the raster for various reasons, such as vectorization, export, and removal.

Raster selections can help you focus on the important parts of the raster data while allowing you to isolate parts of the data you are not interested in. Raster selections can be performed interactively by clicking a series of raster cells or by a Structured Query Language expression-based query using the Select Connected Cells dialog box. Both methods allow you to create a new selection set, add the current selection set, or remove from the current selection set.

Cleaning up the raster data

ArcScan supports tools to perform simple edits on raster layers. One such set of tools is called Raster Cleanup, and it supports its own edit session. Raster cleanup is sometimes essential for raster layers that contain a lot of unwanted cells, commonly referred to as *noise*. You can also use the Raster Cleanup tools to add new raster cells to the image.

Once you have performed the edits on the raster, you can save them to the current file, export the edited raster to a new file, or perform the vectorization and discard all changes. Used in combination with the raster selection tools, Raster Cleanup is a powerful function that can make your vectorization experience more efficient and, therefore, increase productivity.

Using the raster snapping tools

The ability to snap to raster cells has been introduced with the ArcScan extension. This functionality allows you to accurately trace raster data to create vector features, which can enhance the interactive vectorization experience. The supported raster snap agents include centerlines, corners, intersections, ends, and solids.

ArcScan relies on the current Editor snap tolerance settings for raster snapping tolerance. Other settings include showing snap tips, which can help you distinguish what part of a raster's connected cell you are snapped to.

Tracing raster cells

Interactive vectorization is characterized as the process of manually tracing raster cells. This can be accomplished using the standard Editor sketch tools or the ArcScan Vectorization Trace tool. Used in conjunction with raster snapping, raster tracing can be an effective and accurate way to convert raster data to vector features.

Depending on the current edit target layer, you have the option to create line or polygon features. You can also control the geometric composition of the output vector features by adjusting the vectorization settings prior to tracing. Once you have added new features to your database by tracing, you can leverage other tools, such as topology, advanced editing, and spatial adjustment, to modify the data, if necessary.

Batch vectorization

Batch vectorization is defined as an automated technique for converting raster data into vector features. This process relies on user input to control how to perform the vectorization. Factors such as image resolution, amount of noise in the image, and the actual content of the scanned document, all play a role in determining the outcome of the vectorization.

ArcScan supports two vectorization methods: centerline and outline. *Centerline vectorization* will generate vector features along the center of the raster linear elements. *Outline vectorization* will generate vector features at the border of the raster linear elements.

As previously mentioned, the success of a vectorization may be determined by the state of the scanned document at the time of the conversion. It is sometimes necessary to modify the image prior to the generation of features. This process, referred to as *raster preprocessing*, can help you clean up certain portions of the raster that will help define the scope of the vectorization. The Raster Cleanup tools provide the means to perform these steps. Additionally, raster selections can be used in combination or independently of raster cleanup to isolate the raster cells you wish to vectorize.

Besides manipulating the original raster, the most influential factor in batch vectorization is the settings. These settings control which cells are vectorized as well as the amount of generalization and smoothing that is applied to the output vector data. You can modify the settings and preview them immediately in the map to see how they will impact the vectorization. Once you have determined the appropriate settings, you can vectorize the entire raster layer or a defined area of it. After data creation, you can use other Editor tools, such as topology, advanced editing, and spatial adjustment to further refine the data, if necessary.

The ArcScan toolbar

Raster Snapping Options button: Opens the Raster Snapping Options dialog box, which supports raster snapping settings.

Cell Selection menu and tools: Support tools and commands for selecting connected raster cells.

Raster target layer list: Sets the raster layer for selection, cleanup, and vectorization operations.

Vectorization Trace tool: This tool allows you to perform manual raster tracing.

Raster Line Width tool: This tool allows you to view the raster line width for connected cells.

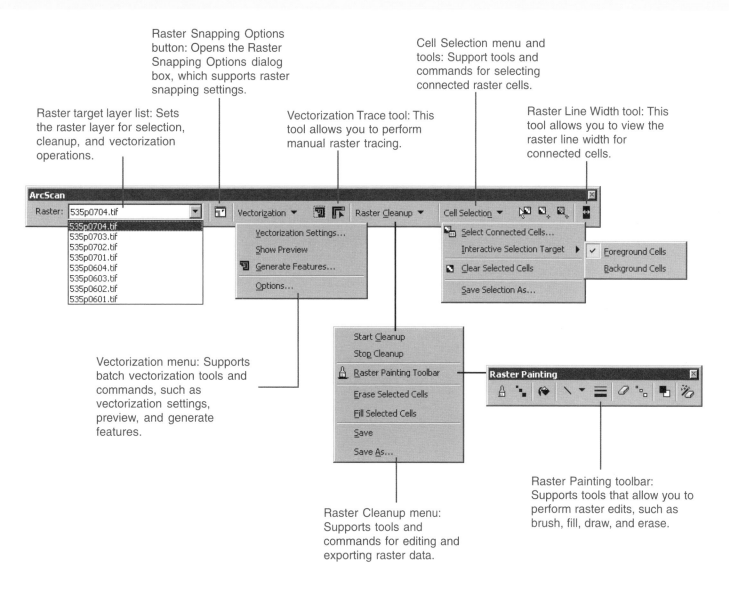

Vectorization menu: Supports batch vectorization tools and commands, such as vectorization settings, preview, and generate features.

Raster Cleanup menu: Supports tools and commands for editing and exporting raster data.

Raster Painting toolbar: Supports tools that allow you to perform raster edits, such as brush, fill, draw, and erase.

How ArcScan works in the editing environment

ArcScan is designed to work in conjunction with the ArcMap Editor. It relies on the Editor menu for many of the functions it supports and is only active when an edit session has been started. This section will describe which Editor tools, commands, and dialog boxes are related to the ArcScan experience.

Starting an edit session

You must start an edit session to activate the ArcScan toolbar and gain access to its tools and commands. If you enable the ArcScan extension while already in an edit session, you must stop editing and restart the edit session to use ArcScan. Click the Editor menu and click Start Editing to start an edit session.

Setting the editing options

ArcScan relies on the Editing Options dialog box to specify the current snap tolerance and stream tolerance and whether or not to show snap tips in the map. Click the Editor menu and click Editing Options to display the Editing Options dialog box.

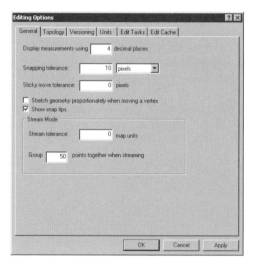

The snapping environment

The raster snapping properties that support the manual vectorization process are located in the Editor Snapping Environment window under the Raster tree. ArcScan supports snapping to raster centerlines, corners, intersections, ends, and solids. Click the Editor menu and click Snapping to display the Snapping Environment window.

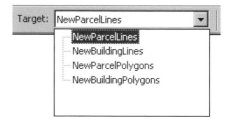

Target layer

Vector features generated by raster tracing will be written to the layer that is specified in the Editor toolbar's Target box. It may be necessary to switch layers when you are creating both line and polygon features during raster tracing. You may also change the target if you wish to vectorize portions of the raster to different vector layers.

Edit tasks

Edit tasks play an important role in the vectorization process. To create features using the Vectorization Trace tool or the Generate Features command, the edit task must be set to Create New Feature. When the features are created, you can switch the edit task to Modify Feature if further editing is required. Click the Editor menu, click the Task dropdown arrow, and choose the appropriate edit task.

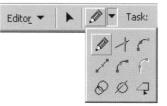

Edit sketch

Although ArcScan supports its own raster tracing tool, you can also use the Editor's Sketch tool to trace raster cells. In cases where you want total control regarding the creation of vertices, the Sketch tool provides this functionality. The Sketch tool will respect the current raster snapping settings to ensure accuracy when creating features.

Undo and redo

As with all the Editor operations, all ArcScan operations can be reversed by using the Undo command. Additionally, the Redo command will reverse the operations previously negated by the Undo command.

Additional editing tools

In addition to the tools and commands available from the Editor toolbar, ArcGIS supports a variety of tools to further extend the editing functionality. These include tools for topology, advanced editing, and spatial adjustment that can assist with editing features once you complete the vectorization. Click the Editor menu and click More Editing Tools to access them.

Saving edits

When you are satisfied with the results of the vectorization, you will need to save the edits to retain the features and any changes you have made to them. You can periodically save edits or wait until you have finished your edit session. Click the Editor menu and click Save Edits.

Adding the Editor toolbar

Before editing geographic feature data within ArcMap, you must first add the Editor toolbar.

Tip

Adding the Editor toolbar from the Tools menu

You can also add the Editor toolbar from the Tools menu. Click Tools and click Editor Toolbar.

Tip

Adding the Editor toolbar from the View menu

You can also add the Editor toolbar by clicking the View menu, pointing to Toolbars, and checking Editor.

Tip

Adding the Editor toolbar using the Customize dialog box

Click the Tools menu and click Customize. Click the Toolbars tab and check the Editor check box.

1. Start ArcMap.
2. Click the Editor Toolbar button to display the Editor toolbar.
3. Click the toolbar's title bar and drag it to the top of the ArcMap application window.

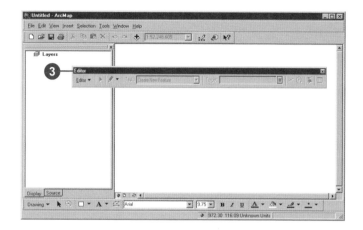

Starting and stopping an edit session

All editing takes place within an *edit session*. To begin, choose Start Editing from the Editor menu. The edits you make are immediately visible on your map but are not saved to the database until you choose to do so.

If you're working with large amounts of data, you can speed up the editing and selection of features by creating an edit cache. An *edit cache* holds the features visible in the current map extent in memory on your local machine. An edit cache results in faster editing because ArcMap doesn't have to retrieve data from the server. ▶

Tip

Editing a map with more than one collection of datasets

You can only edit one collection of datasets—one workspace—at a time. These can be geodatabases and shapefiles. If your map contains more than one collection, when you choose Start Editing you will be prompted to choose which one you want to edit.

Starting an edit session

1. Start ArcMap and add the Editor toolbar.

2. Click Editor and click Start Editing.

    The Editor toolbar is now active.

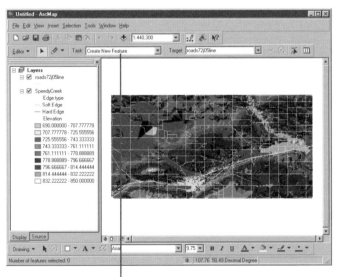

The Editor toolbar is now active.

You can create an edit cache by clicking the Build Edit Cache command on the Edit Cache toolbar. When you're finished editing, you can save any changes you've made or quit editing without saving. You can also save the edits you've made at any time by choosing Save Edits from the Editor menu.

Tip

Zooming to your edit cache extent

You can quickly return to your edit cache extent at any time in your edit session. Click the Zoom to Edit Cache button on the Edit Cache toolbar.

Creating an edit cache

1. Add the data you want to edit.
2. Click the Zoom In button on the Tools toolbar.
3. Zoom in to the area on the map that you want to edit.
4. Click the Build Edit Cache button on the Edit Cache toolbar.

   The features visible in the current extent are held in memory locally.

Saving your edits in the middle of an edit session

1. Click Editor.
2. Click Save Edits.

   Any edits you have made are saved to the database.

Stopping an edit session

1. Click Editor and click Stop Editing.

2. To save changes, click Yes. To quit without saving, click No.

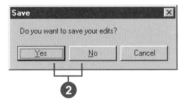

Enabling the ArcScan extension

Before you can start using ArcScan, you must enable the ArcScan extension in ArcMap.

The ArcScan extension is only available for the ArcEditor and ArcInfo licenses. You can change your ArcGIS license by using the Desktop Administrator tool.

Tip

Enabling the ArcScan extension while in an edit session

If you enable the ArcScan extension while already in an edit session, the ArcScan extension will not be activated until you stop and restart the edit session.

See Also

For information on ArcGIS extensions, see the ArcGIS Desktop Help topic 'Using ArcGIS extensions'.

1. Click the Tools menu and click Extensions.

2. Check ArcScan.

3. Click Close.

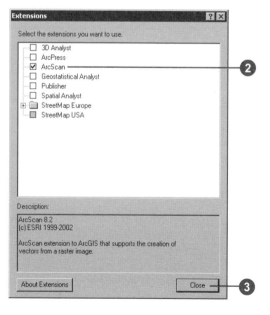

Adding the ArcScan toolbar

Before using the ArcScan tools and commands, you must first add the ArcScan toolbar.

The ArcScan toolbar will become active only when the following conditions exist:

- The ArcScan extension is enabled.

- An edit session has been started.

- At least one raster layer and one vector layer (line or polygon) has been added to the map.

- The target raster layer has been symbolized into two unique colors.

Tip

Are there other ways to add the ArcScan toolbar?

You can add the ArcScan toolbar to ArcMap by clicking the Tools menu and clicking Customize. In the Customize dialog box, click the Toolbars tab, check the ArcScan check box, and click Close.

1. Click View, point to Toolbars, and click ArcScan.

   The ArcScan toolbar will appear in the map.

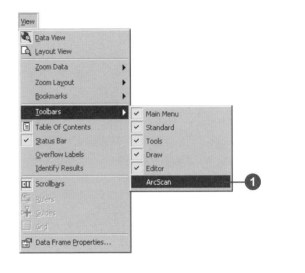

Changing the raster layer symbology

Before you can start working with your raster layer in ArcScan, you must ensure that the raster's layer symbology is displayed as two unique colors. The ArcScan toolbar will become active once the symbology is changed.

This is required since ArcScan only supports bi-level raster imagery. ArcScan will support any two colors so long as they are unique colors with unique color values. You can use the Unique Values rendering option to display the raster as two unique colors. You can also use the Classified rendering option to display the raster as two classes.

See Also

For more details on symbolizing raster data in ArcMap, see Using ArcMap.

1. In the table of contents, right-click the raster layer and click Properties.

2. Click the Symbology tab.

3. In the Show box, click the Unique Values option.

4. Click OK.

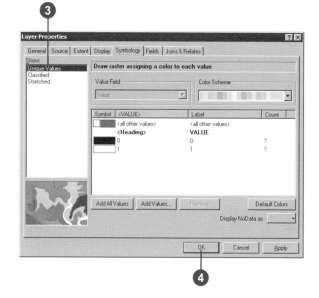

Working with multiband rasters

When working with multiband rasters (RGB Composite), only add one band from the raster dataset to the map and classify the layer as two classes.

Setting the classified rendering option

1. In the table of contents, right-click the raster layer and click Properties.

2. Click the Symbology tab.

3. In the Show box, click the Classified option.

4. In the Classification box, click the Classes dropdown arrow and click 2.

5. Click OK.

Selecting the target raster layer

ArcScan requires that you choose a target raster layer prior to using the ArcScan tools and commands. The target raster layer will be used for raster selections, raster cleanup, and vectorization.

This choice is available on the ArcScan toolbar's Raster section. All raster layers that have been symbolized to display unique colors will be available in the Raster dropdown list. If your map only contains one raster layer, it will be set as the target raster layer by default.

1. Click the ArcScan toolbar and click the Raster dropdown arrow.

2. Click the target raster layer.

   The target raster layer will now be displayed in the Raster dropdown list.

Setting the vectorization options

ArcScan supports two vectorization methods for batch mode: centerline and outline.

The centerline vectorization method allows you to generate vector line features at the center of the raster cells. The centerline vectorization method is the default setting.

The outline vectorization method allows you to generate vector polygon features at the borders of the raster cells. ▶

Tip

Adding data to support the vectorization methods

Each vectorization method requires certain data types to which to write. The centerline method requires that an editable line layer exists in the map. The outline method requires that an editable polygon layer exists in the map.

Changing the vectorization method

1. Click the Vectorization menu and click Options.

2. Click a vectorization method.

3. Click OK.

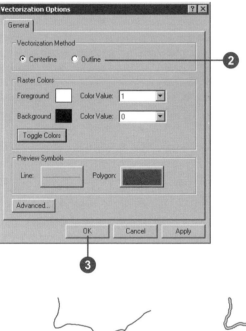

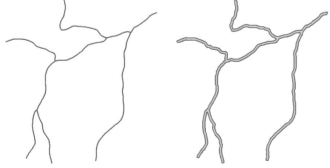

Examples of centerline and outline vectorization of river data

Since ArcScan supports bi-level raster imagery, the notion of foreground and background colors is important.

By default, ArcScan will use the foreground color for raster selections, raster cleanup, and vectorization. Typically, the foreground color will represent the raster cells that are to be vectorized. However, there may be cases when you will need to switch the foreground and background raster colors. You switch raster colors by using the Toggle Colors command that is available in the Vectorization Options dialog box. ▶

Tip

Automatic foreground and background colors

ArcMap will automatically determine the foreground color by comparing the number of pixels in each symbol. The symbol that has the lesser number of pixels will be designated as the foreground color.

See Also

For more information on toggling raster colors, see 'Using the Raster Painting tools' in Chapter 5.

Toggling the raster foreground and background colors

1. Click the Vectorization menu and click Options.

2. Click Toggle Colors.

3. Click OK.

You can change the line and polygon symbols that are used for the vectorization preview in the Vectorization Options dialog box. This allows you to customize the preview symbology so that it will differentiate from other feature layer symbology that is present in the map.

The Symbol Selector dialog box will appear when you click the symbol buttons located in the Preview Symbols section. For lines, you can change the symbol, color, and width. For polygons, you can change the symbol, fill color, outline width, and outline color. ►

Tip

Hiding the preview symbols

You can hide the preview symbols by setting the symbol color properties (i.e., color, fill color, outline color) to No Color.

See Also

For more information on modifying symbols, see Using ArcMap.

Changing the preview symbols

1. Click the Vectorization menu and click Options.

2. Click Line or Polygon.

3. In the Symbol Selector dialog box, click a new symbol or change specific properties of the symbol.

4. Click OK to close the Symbol Selector dialog box.

5. Click OK.

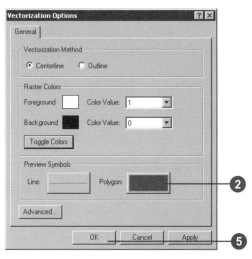

The Advanced Options dialog box allows you to specify the maximum number of vertices that will be used to construct polygon features during batch vectorization.

By default, this setting is enabled and uses a value of 100000 for the maximum number of vertices a polygon feature can have. This value can be increased by manually entering a smaller or larger value depending on the input raster data. If this value is exceeded during vectorization, ArcScan will generate line features in place of polygon features.

Tip

Disabling the Advanced Options

You can disable the Maximum Number of Vertices in a Polygon setting by unchecking the check box in the Advanced Options dialog box.

Tip

Maintaining optimal performance

Vectorization performance may be adversely affected if the Maximum Number of Vertices in a Polygon setting is disabled. It is recommended that this setting remain enabled for optimal vectorization and ArcMap performance.

Setting the advanced options

1. Click the Vectorization menu and click Options.

2. Click Advanced.

3. Enter a new value for the Maximum Number of Vertices in a Polygon setting.

4. Click OK to close the Advanced Options dialog box.

5. Click OK.

Raster tracing

4

ArcScan provides the tools required to perform interactive vectorization. This process, referred to as *raster tracing*, allows you to create vector features along the centerline of connected raster cells. Raster tracing gives you total control over the vectorization process and is enhanced by the raster snapping capabilities introduced with ArcScan. Raster tracing is intended for those who need to vectorize dense areas of the raster or portions of the raster where noise or other cells overlap the target raster lines. It is also designed for those who prefer to closely manage the creation of vector data.

This chapter provides an introduction on how to use ArcScan raster snapping and tracing tools. It covers the raster snapping environment, determining raster line widths, and using the Sketch and Vectorization Trace tools to create line and polygon features.

An overview of raster tracing

Raster tracing involves the manual creation of features assisted by the ability to snap to raster cells. Raster tracing is typically employed when the user wants total control of the vectorization process or only needs to vectorize a small area of the raster image. It can also be used in situations where the resolution of the scanned image is poor and, therefore, requires careful digitizing to ensure the appropriate raster cells are traced and integrated into the vector-based feature layer.

Raster tracing allows a higher level of flexibility for vectorization since you can use the Editor's Sketch tool or the ArcScan Vectorization Trace tool to generate features.

Editing options

ArcScan relies on settings supported in the Editing Options dialog box. These include settings for snapping tolerance, stream tolerance, and snap tips. Since the ArcScan extension is specific to raster data, snapping tolerance should be set to pixels.

Raster snapping

Raster snapping was introduced by ArcScan to provide an accurate way to trace connected cells. The ability to snap to connected cells can help make interactive vectorization more efficient.

The raster snapping properties are set in the Editor's Snapping Environment window under the Raster snap agent tree. You can choose to snap to the following locations of raster connected cells: centerlines, corners, ends, intersections, and solids.

Raster snapping allows you to accurately create features that follow the middle of the raster linear elements. The Editor's Snapping tolerance applies to both vector and raster snapping properties.

Raster snapping options

ArcScan also supports its own snapping options that are specific to raster tracing. These can be found in the Raster Snapping Options dialog box, which is accessible from the ArcScan toolbar. These options include settings for the foreground and background colors, maximum raster line width, solid diameter range, and hole size. Maximum raster line width is an important setting for vectorization. Since ArcScan will only recognize lines that are less than or equal to the maximum line width value, raster linear elements that do not meet this criteria cannot be snapped to or traced.

Target layer

Another setting that ArcScan relies on is the target layer, which is located on the Editor toolbar. Features created with the Sketch and Vectorization Trace tools will be written to the current target layer. Target layers can be line and polygon feature layers.

Using the Sketch tool to trace rasters

You can use the Sketch tool to trace raster cells and create vector features. This method provides total control of where vertices are constructed for the feature. With the exception of snapping to raster cells, the Sketch tool will behave as it does during typical vector-based feature editing. All of the functionality supported by the Sketch tool is still available when using it within the ArcScan environment.

Vectorization settings

Vectorization settings allow you to influence the structure of the output vector features. These settings apply to both interactive and batch vectorization processes. In raster tracing, vectorization settings only impact features that are created using the Vectorization Trace tool. These settings do not influence features that are created using the Sketch tool.

Vectorization settings allow you to fine-tune the outcome of the raster-to-vector conversion. You can use them to control which raster cells are available for vectorization, the degree of generalization and smoothing used to create vector features, and how to deal with atypical characteristics of the raster.

Using the Vectorization Trace tool

The Vectorization Trace tool is designed as the main component of the raster tracing task. It is similiar to the Sketch tool in regards to starting and finishing a sketch. However, its usage goes beyond that by providing specific functionality to make the tracing of raster cells an efficient process.

Once an appropriate raster snapping environment is set up, you can begin tracing raster cells by clicking at a start location and pointing the vectorization tool in the direction you wish to trace. The tool will follow the centerline of the raster linear element and create vertices at various locations based on the current vectorization settings. This process is much faster than traditional digitizing methods since it will create features continuously until it reaches the next raster intersection or the end of the raster line. In cases where it encounters a noncontiguous area of the raster linear element, it will prompt you to direct the trace tool to a new start location. This semiautomated method for tracing raster cells can help save you time and increase productivity.

Saving edits

As with standard editing practices, any new features created during the vectorization process must be saved to the database. You can save edits during the edit session or wait until you stop editing.

The Snapping Environment window

You can keep the window open as you work— any changes in settings are effective immediately. Click Close when you are finished.

The layers in your map document are listed here. Set the snapping priority— the order in which snapping will occur by layer—by dragging the layer names to new locations.

The Edit Sketch tree shows snapping properties that work with a sketch.

The Raster tree shows snapping properties that work with raster cells.

Check the type of snapping properties you want for each layer.

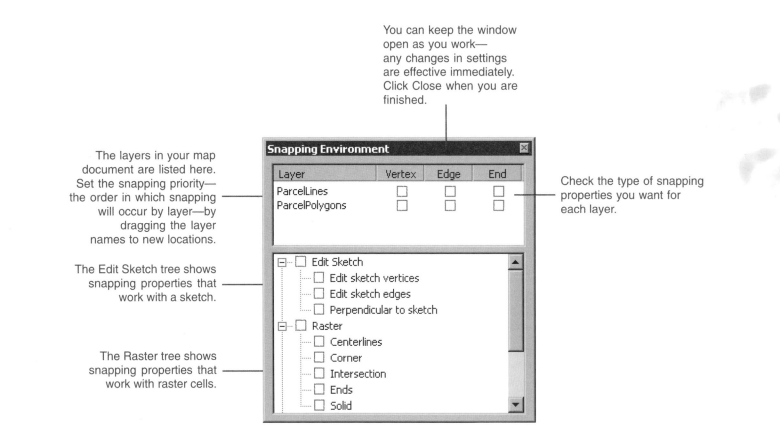

Types of snapping properties

When you use the snapping environment to create or place a new feature in an exact location relative to other features, you must choose to which part of existing features—vertex, edge, or endpoint—you want your feature to snap. These choices are called layer snapping properties. You can also specify snapping properties for the edit sketch itself; these are called sketch snapping properties. You can set both types of snapping properties using the Snapping Environment window. The following table briefly explains each of the layer snapping and sketch snapping properties.

Layer snapping properties		Sketch snapping properties	
Vertex	Snaps to each vertex of the features in that layer.	Perpendicular to sketch	Lets you create a segment that will be perpendicular to the previous segment.
Edge	Snaps to the entire outline—both segments and vertices—of each feature in that layer.	Edit sketch vertices	Snaps to the vertices of the sketch.
Endpoint	Snaps to the first vertex and the last vertex in a line feature.	Edit sketch edges	Snaps to the entire outline—both segments and vertices—of the sketch.

Types of raster snapping properties

When you use the snapping environment to trace raster data, you must choose to which part of the raster element you want your sketch or trace tool to snap. These choices are called raster snapping properties. You can set these raster snapping properties using the Snapping Environment window. The following table briefly explains the raster snapping properties.

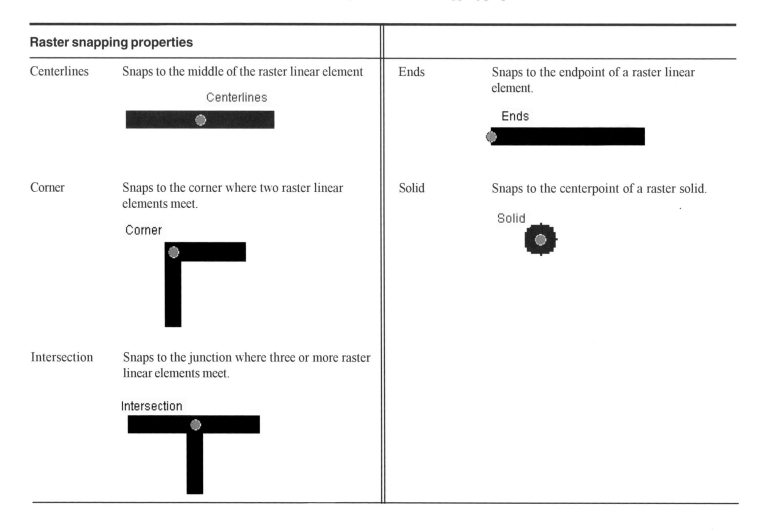

Raster snapping properties

Centerlines	Snaps to the middle of the raster linear element	Ends	Snaps to the endpoint of a raster linear element.
Corner	Snaps to the corner where two raster linear elements meet.	Solid	Snaps to the centerpoint of a raster solid.
Intersection	Snaps to the junction where three or more raster linear elements meet.		

Using the snapping environment

The *snapping environment* can help you establish exact locations in relation to other features. Setting the snapping environment involves setting a snapping tolerance, snapping properties, and a snapping priority.

The *snapping tolerance* is the distance within which the pointer or a feature is snapped to another location. If the location being snapped to (vertex, intersection, or centerline) is within the distance you set, the pointer automatically snaps (jumps) to the location. ▶

Tip

Viewing the snapping tolerance
To see the current snapping tolerance, hold down the T key while using the Sketch tool.

Setting the snapping tolerance

1. Click Editor and click Options.
2. Click the General tab.
3. Click the Snapping tolerance dropdown arrow and click the type of measurement unit you want to use for the snapping tolerance—pixels or map units.

   Pixel measurement units are recommended for use with raster snapping.
4. Type the desired number of measurement units in the Snapping tolerance text box.
5. Click OK.

Editing Options

General | Topology | Versioning | Units | Edit Tasks | Edit Cache

Display measurements using [4] decimal places

Snapping tolerance: [10] pixels

Sticky move tolerance: [0] pixels

☐ Stretch geometry proportionately when moving a vertex
☑ Show snap tips.

Stream Mode

Stream tolerance: [0] map units

Group [50] points together when streaming

OK   Cancel   Apply

The circle around the pointer in the graphics below represents the snapping tolerance. When the location being snapped to (orange point) is outside the snapping tolerance, the snapping location (blue dot) stays with the pointer (top graphic). When the location being snapped to is inside the snapping tolerance, the snapping location moves away from the pointer and snaps to the target location (bottom graphic).

You can choose the part of the feature—vertex, edge, or endpoint—to which you want your new feature to snap by setting the layer *snapping properties*. When tracing rasters, you can choose the part of the connected cells— centerline, corner, intersection, end, or solid—to which you want your new feature to snap by setting the Raster snapping properties. ▶

Setting snapping properties

1. Click Editor and click Snapping.

   The Snapping Environment window appears.

2. Check the snapping properties you want.

   The snapping properties are effective as soon as they are checked or unchecked.

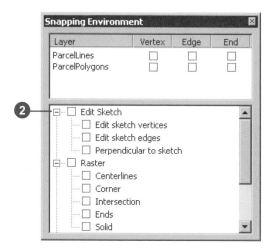

You can also set the *snapping priority* for layers on your map. The order of layers listed in the Snapping Environment window determines the order in which snapping will occur. Snapping occurs first in the layer at the top of the list and then in each consecutive layer down the list. You can easily change the snapping priority by dragging the layer names to new locations.

Tip

Sketch snapping properties

You can set snapping properties that apply specifically to an edit sketch in the Snapping Environment dialog box as well; these are located at the bottom of the Snapping Environment window. For more information, see 'Types of snapping properties' in this chapter.

Setting the snapping priority

1. Click Editor and click Snapping.

   The Snapping Environment window appears.

2. Click and drag the layer names to arrange them in the order in which you want snapping to occur. (The first layer in the list will be snapped to first.)

   The snapping priorities you set are effective immediately.

Setting the raster snapping options

ArcScan supports a separate options dialog box for raster snapping. The Raster Snapping Options dialog box is accessible from the ArcScan toolbar, and it allows you to apply settings that are specific to the raster tracing experience.

The first option in this dialog box is for toggling the raster foreground and background colors. Raster tracing only works on foreground colors, so this tool allows you to switch the desired color to foreground status without having to change the raster layer symbology. ►

Toggling raster foreground and background colors

1. Click the ArcScan toolbar and click the Raster Snapping Options button.

2. Click the Toggle Colors button.

   The foreground and background color graphics will switch.

3. Click OK.

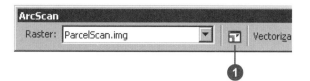

The next option in the dialog box pertains to specifying a maximum raster line width for tracing. Based on the value you enter, ArcScan will only allow you to snap to raster lines that are equal to or less than the maximum line width value. This allows you to control which lines can be snapped to and ultimately vectorized based on their line width. ▶

Tip

How can I determine an appropriate maximum raster line width?

You can use the Raster Line Width tool to determine the line width for a series of connected cells. For more information about this tool, see 'Using the Raster Line Width tool' in this chapter.

Specifying the maximum raster line width

1. Click the ArcScan toolbar and click the Raster Snapping Options button.

2. Enter a value for the maximum raster line width.

3. Click OK.

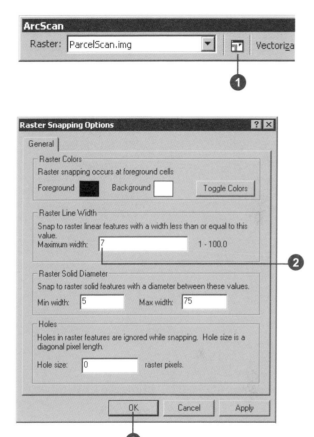

Similiar to the raster line width setting, ArcScan also provides a setting for snapping to solids. Solids are a series of raster cells that represent circular features. In some cases, there may be elements in the raster that qualify as a circle but are not in the scope of the vectorization (i.e., periods, dots, etc.). ArcScan allows you to specify a minimum and maximum range for solid diameters. Any solid whose diameter falls within this range will be recognized as a solid and will be available for snapping. ►

Tip

Determining solid diameter
You can use the Solid Diameter tool to determine the diameter for raster solids. This tool can be added via the ArcScan commands available in the Customize dialog box.

Specifying the minimum and maximum solid diameters

1. Click the ArcScan toolbar and click the Raster Snapping Options button.

2. Enter a value for the minimum solid diameter.

3. Enter a value for the maximum solid diameter.

4. Click OK.

ArcScan provides a way to ignore holes that exist in raster linear elements when tracing with the Vectorization Trace tool. Hole size is measured as the diagonal distance of the background cells in pixels. Holes that are less than the specified size will be ignored, and the Vectorization Trace tool will continue to trace the connected cells. Holes may appear in areas of the raster that represent lines due to poor resolution.

Raster lines containing holes

Tip

Filling holes before tracing
You can use the Raster Cleanup tools to fill in holes prior to vectorization. See 'Using the Raster Cleanup commands' in Chapter 5, 'Batch vectorization'.

Specifying the hole size

1. Click the ArcScan toolbar and click the Raster Snapping Options button.

2. Enter a value for the hole size that you want ignored during tracing.

3. Click OK.

Raster Snapping Options

General

Raster Colors
Raster snapping occurs at foreground cells

Foreground   Background   Toggle Colors

Raster Line Width
Snap to raster linear features with a width less than or equal to this value.
Maximum width: 7   1 - 100.0

Raster Solid Diameter
Snap to raster solid features with a diameter between these values.

Min width: 5   Max width: 75

Holes
Holes in raster features are ignored while snapping. Hole size is a diagonal pixel length.

Hole size: 0   raster pixels.

OK   Cancel   Apply

Using the Raster Line Width tool

You can find the width of any raster linear element using the Raster Line Width tool. This tool allows you to display the width of raster lines so you can determine an appropriate maximum line width value setting. This tool is applicable for both raster tracing and batch vectorization.

To use the tool, click the Raster Line Width tool located on the ArcScan toolbar and place the cursor over a raster line. A map tip will display the width of the line in raster pixels.

Tip

Using raster snapping for more accurate cursor placement

You can use raster snapping to help you display the raster line widths. This can help by allowing you to snap to the raster lines for which you wish to display the width.

Determining the raster line width

1. Click the ArcScan toolbar and click the Raster Line Width tool.

2. Place the cursor over a series of connected raster cells that represent a line element.

   The raster line width will be displayed in a map tip as pixels.

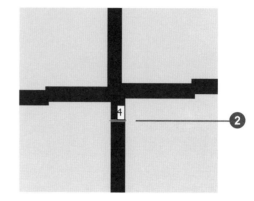

Setting the maximum line width

1. Click the ArcScan toolbar and click the Raster Line Width tool.

2. Place the cursor over a series of connected raster cells that represent a line element and left-click.

3. If the raster line width value is acceptable, press Enter; otherwise, enter a new value and press Enter.

   This will set the maximum line width value in the Vectorization Settings dialog box based on the value you enter.

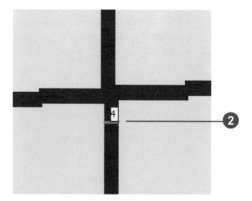

An overview of the vectorization settings

Vectorization settings are one of the most important components of the ArcScan extension. These settings allow you to dictate which raster data can be vectorized and how the geometry of output vector data should be constructed. No other settings in ArcScan impact the outcome of the raster-to-vector conversion as do the vectorization settings.

Vectorization settings apply to both raster tracing and batch vectorization. When performing raster tracing, you can see how the settings apply as you trace over the raster cells. In batch vectorization the same will apply, however, on a larger scale since a considerable portion of the raster layer will be vectorized, if not the entire layer. The vectorization settings can be entered and applied through the modeless Vectorization Settings dialog box. You can make changes to these settings and see the effects immediately in the map by using the Show Preview command.

Once you have established the appropriate settings for your data, you can proceed with the vectorization. The settings that you established can be saved as styles and reused on similar data.

Intersection solution

The Intersection Solution setting determines how ArcScan will generate features that meet at a junction. An *intersection* is defined as three or more raster linear elements that meet at a common point. The corner of a shared parcel boundary is one example of this.

The Vectorization Settings support three types of intersection solutions: Geometrical, Median, and None. The Geometrical intersection solution is designed to preserve angles and straight lines. This option would be typically used for engineering drawings and street maps. The Median intersection solution is designed to work with nonrectilinear angles. This option would be typically used for natural resource maps (i.e., vegetation, soil, tributary maps). The None intersection solution is designed for rasters that have nonintersection features. This option would typically be used for contour maps.

Examples of Geometrical, Median, and None intersection solutions

Vectorization Settings

Intersection Solution:	Geometrical ▼	
Maximum Line Width:	20	1 - 100.0
☑ Compression Tolerance:	0.025	0.001 - 50.0
☑ Smoothing Weight:	3	1 - 20.0
☑ Gap Closure Tolerance:	10	1 - 1000.0
Fan Angle:	60	0 - 180.0
Hole Size:	5	0 - 100.0

Styles...   Load or save a pre-defined vectorization style

About Vectorization   Apply   Close

The Vectorization Settings dialog box

Maximum line width

The Maximum Line Width setting allows you to specify which raster linear elements are eligible for raster tracing. Raster linear elements that are less than or equal to the maximum line width value will qualify for raster snapping and tracing operations. For batch vectorization, raster linear elements that have a width less than or equal to the maximum line width value will be eligible for centerline vectorization. All other raster linear elements will be vectorized as polygon features if an editable polygon layer exists in the map.

The Maximum Line Width setting can be used as a filter in cases where you want to omit larger, thicker lines and only vectorize the thinner lines in the raster. This setting also affects the construction of the output features, so it is important to use the most accurate value possible for the data with which you are working. You can determine the widths of raster lines by using the Raster Line Width tool. This tool allows you to display the width of the raster via a map tip. If you click on a line with this tool, a small Raster Line Width input box will appear. You can leave this value unchanged or type in a new value and update the Maximum Line Width setting by pressing Enter. This technique can help you save time by allowing you to update line width settings without having to open the Vectorization Settings dialog box.

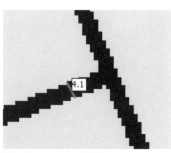

The Raster Line Width tool

Compression tolerance

Compression Tolerance is the most significant setting for influencing the output vector feature geometry. This setting is used to reduce the number of vertices of line features that are generated during the vectorization process. Compression is a vector postprocessing procedure that uses a Douglas–Peucker generalization algorithm with a specified maximum allowable offset given as input. The compressed output is a subset of the original input vertices. Using larger Compression Tolerance values will reduce the number of vertices that are used to construct line features. A reduction of vertices will cause the output line features to differ from the original shape of the source lines. The Compression Tolerance value does not represent map or pixel units; rather, it represents an intensity level of the generalization.

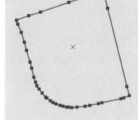

Portion of scanned parcel map

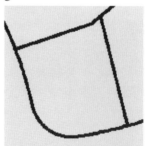

Compression Tolerance = .025

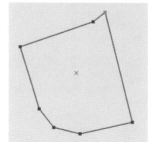

Compression Tolerance = 1

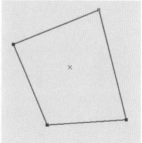

Compression Tolerance = 10

Smoothing weight

This setting is used to smooth line features that are generated during the vectorization process. Using larger Smoothing Weight values will result in smoother line features. However, using larger Smoothing Weights may cause the output line features to differ from the original shape of the source line. The Smoothing Weight value does not represent map or pixel units; rather, it represents an intensity level of the smoothing.

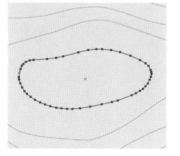

Portion of scanned contour map

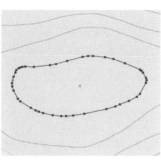

Smoothing Weight = 1

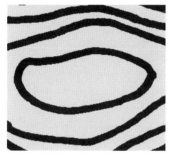

Smoothing Weight = 3

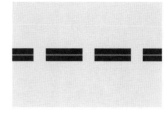

Smoothing Weight = 10

Gap closure tolerance

The cells that represent lines in the raster may contain gaps. In most cases, these gaps are a result of the poor quality of the

source document or scanning process. However, sometimes gaps may be part of an original document's line symbology. One example would be the use of dashed lines to represent utility lines.

The Gap Closure Tolerance is a distance in pixels that is used to jump over breaks in a raster line. Based on the value you enter, gaps that are less than or equal to the Gap Closure Tolerance will be closed during vectorization. However, gaps will not be closed in places where lines intersect. This setting applies to raster tracing and batch vectorization.

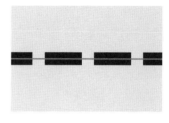

Gap Closure setting disabled   Gap Closure setting enabled

Fan angle

You can add additional intelligence to the gap closure function by using the Fan Angle setting. Based on an angle you specify, the gap closure function will use it to search for raster lines when jumping over gaps. This can be useful in cases where the raster line you are vectorizing is curved and contains gaps.

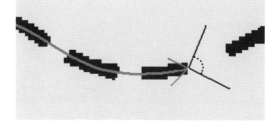

Example of how the Fan Angle tool works

Holes

ArcScan provides a way to ignore holes in raster lines during vectorization. *Holes* are small gaps in the raster line that are completely surrounded by the foreground pixels. These may be caused by the poor quality of the source document or scanning process. Holes that possess a diagonal length less than or equal to the specified distance will be treated as part of the raster line when vectorized. The choice to ignore holes is only available for raster snapping and tracing.

Hole size = 0   Hole size = 5

Styles

Once you have determined the optimal vectorization settings for the data you are working with, you can save this information using the Styles command. These styles can then be loaded and reused. This design helps you save time by providing the ability to retain these settings so you do not have to reenter them. Additionally, you can create styles for various types of rasters that are specific to a particular discipline. For instance, if you work with contour maps on a regular basis, you can create a style for this raster data type and use it for other contour maps that you need to vectorize.

ArcScan also provides predefined styles that are based on various types of raster data. These include contours, parcels, outlines, and polygons. When you load these predefined styles, the vectorization settings will automatically be updated. Predefined styles can be used as is or modified and saved as new styles.

Applying the vectorization settings for raster tracing

Raster tracing is most affected by the vectorization settings that you apply. In the following pages you will see the steps to take to apply each of these settings.

Tip

A modeless Vectorization Settings dialog box
The modeless design of the Vectorization Settings dialog box allows you to continually update the settings and apply the changes without having to reopen it.

See Also

For more information about using the Raster Line Width tool, see 'Using the Raster Line Width tool' in this chapter.

Specifying the maximum line width

1. Click the Vectorization menu and click Vectorization Settings.

2. Enter a value for the Maximum Line Width.

3. Click Apply.

4. Click Close.

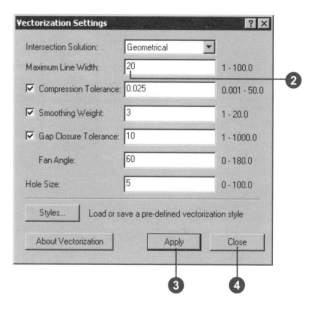

Setting the compression tolerance

1. Click the Vectorization menu and click Vectorization Settings.

2. Check the Compression Tolerance box.

3. Enter a value for the Compression Tolerance.

4. Click Apply.

5. Click Close.

Setting the smoothing weight

1. Click the Vectorization menu and click Vectorization Settings.

2. Check the Smoothing Weight box.

3. Enter a value for the Smoothing Weight.

4. Click Apply.

5. Click Close.

Setting the gap closure tolerance and fan angle

1. Click the Vectorization menu and click Vectorization Settings.

2. Check the Gap Closure Tolerance box.

3. Enter a value for the Gap Closure Tolerance.

4. Enter a value for the Fan Angle.

5. Click Apply.

6. Click Close.

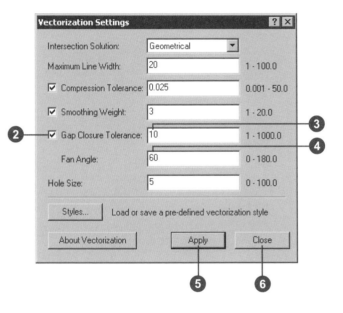

Setting the hole size

1. Click the Vectorization menu and click Vectorization Settings.

2. Enter a value for the Hole Size.

3. Click Apply.

4. Click Close.

Creating line features using raster snapping and the Sketch tool

You can use the Editor's Sketch tool to trace rasters and create line features. This requires the current edit target to point to a line feature layer. This process relies on appropriate raster snapping settings to ensure that you create features along the centerlines of the raster linear elements.

In addition to snapping to centerlines, you can snap to intersections, ends, and solids. Using the Sketch tool, you can control where vertices are created by clicking at desired locations. To ensure accurate tracing, you should increase the number of vertices for curved raster linear elements.

Tip

Displaying snapping properties

Enable the Show snap tips option to display to which raster snap property your cursor is snapped. This setting is located in the Editing Options dialog box.

1. Click the Editor toolbar and click the Sketch tool.
2. Snap to a location in the raster layer.
3. Click once to start creating the line feature. ▶

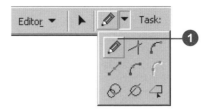

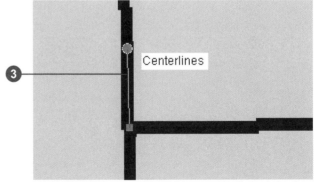

See Also

For more information about creating features with the Sketch tool, see Editing in ArcMap.

4. Click at locations where you wish to create vertices.

5. When you reach the final destination, press F2 to finish the sketch.

   A line feature that follows the raster linear element is now created.

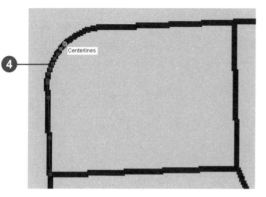

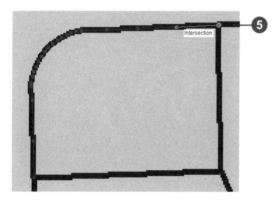

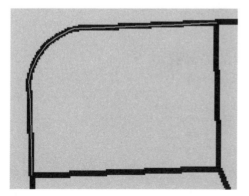

Creating polygon features using raster snapping and the Sketch tool

You can use the Editor's Sketch tool to trace rasters and create polygon features. This requires the current edit target to point to a polygon feature layer. This process relies on appropriate raster snapping settings to ensure that you create features along the centerlines of the raster linear elments.

In addition to snapping to centerlines, you can snap to intersections, ends, and solids. Using the Sketch tool, you can control where vertices are created by clicking at desired locations. To ensure accurate tracing, you should increase the number of vertices for curved raster linear elements.

Tip

Snapping to intersections first

It is recommended that you start creating polygon features at intersections when possible. Since intersections have the highest trace priority, this will ensure that the start and end points share the same coordinates.

1. Click the Editor toolbar and click the Sketch tool.

2. Snap to a location in the raster layer.

3. Click once to start creating the polygon feature. ▶

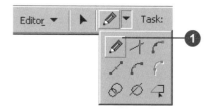

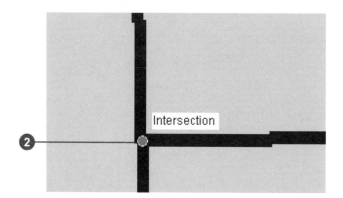

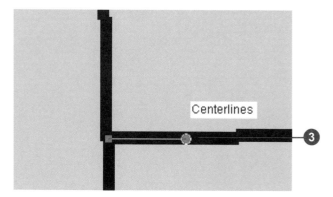

4. Click at locations where you wish to create vertices.

5. When you reach the final destination, press F2 to finish the sketch.

   A polygon feature that follows the raster linear element is now created.

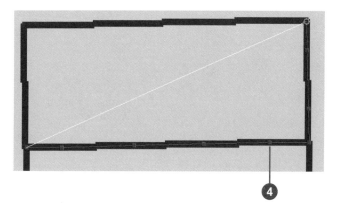

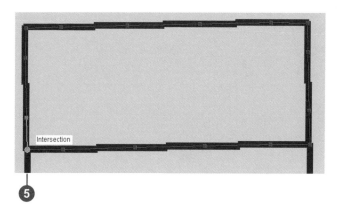

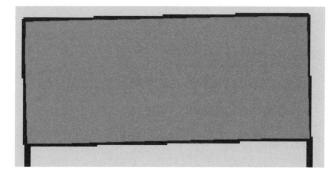

Creating line features using the Vectorization Trace tool

The Vectorization Trace tool is specifically designed for tracing connected raster cells. Just place the tool at an appropriate start location in the raster and click once to begin the tracing process. The Vectorization Trace tool will automatically follow the centerline of the raster cells based on the direction you point the tool's arrow and subsequently generate vector features.

Using raster snapping in conjunction with the Vectorization Trace tool is highly recommended. However, it is not necessary. The Vectorization Trace tool will recognize contiguous raster cells on its own and create features without the use of raster snapping properties. ▶

Tip

Using raster snapping
It is highly recommended that you use raster snapping in conjunction with the Vectorization Trace tool for accurate results.

1. Click the Editor toolbar and click the Vectorization Trace tool.

2. Snap to a location in the raster layer.

3. Click once to activate the Vectorization Trace tool.

4. Point the tool's arrowhead in the direction you wish to trace. ▶

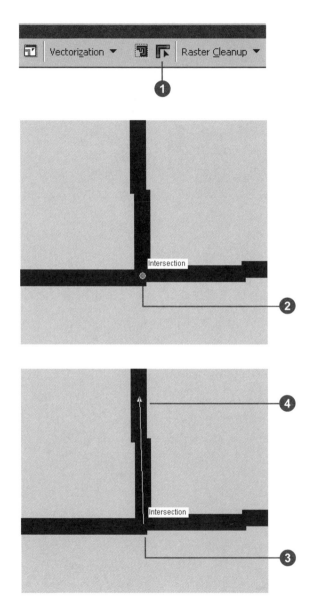

The Vectorization Trace tool works by following along the middle or centerline of a series of connected raster cells. When you click the tool, a cursor will appear that is similiar to the standard edit sketch cursor. Once you snap to a location or place your cursor over a raster cell, click once to begin the trace. An arrowhead at the end of the line will appear. Point the arrow in the direction you wish to trace and click once to begin creating features. The Vectorization Trace tool will create features along the raster linear element until it (a) reaches the end of the raster linear element or (b) encounters a raster intersection. You can finish the sketch at this point or continue by repeating these steps. ▸

Tip

Why does the Vectorization Trace tool ignore some raster cells?

Raster cells that are ignored during tracing could be exceeding the maximum raster line width setting. You can change this value via the Vectorization Settings dialog box.

See Also

For more information about influencing the output geometry of vector features, see 'An overview of the vectorization settings' in this chapter.

5. Click once to start tracing.

   The Vectorization Trace tool automatically creates vertices based on the current vectorization settings.

6. If you encounter an intersection, the Vectorization Trace tool stops. Point the arrow in the direction you wish to vectorize and click once to continue tracing. ▸

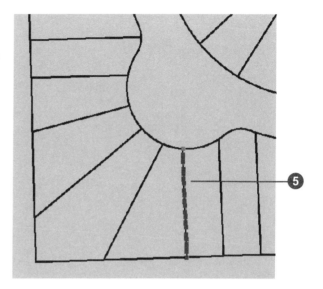

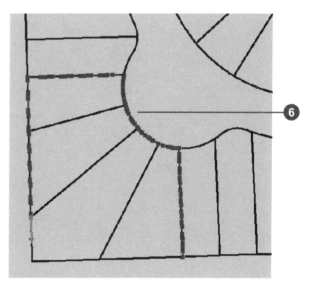

Depending on the current vectorization settings, the location and number of vertices in the line feature will vary. You can change these settings via the Vectorization settings dialog box to improve the outcome of the tracing.

Once you have finished tracing, press F2 to finish the sketch. The next time you save your edits, the line feature will be added to the target feature layer.

Tip

Finishing the sketch with the Vectorization Trace tool

Besides pressing the F2 key, you can also double-click to end the sketch. Additionally, you can right-click with the trace tool active to open the tool's context menu and click the Finish Sketch command.

7. When you have reached the end of the raster line or the start point of the sketch, press F2 to finish the sketch.

   A vector line feature now represents the connected raster cells.

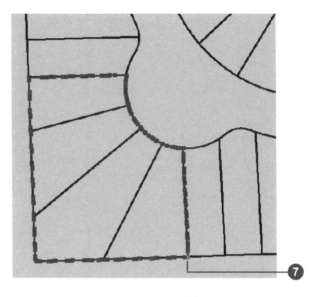

Creating polygon features using the Vectorization Trace tool

The Vectorization Trace tool is specifically designed for tracing connected raster cells. Just place the tool at an appropriate start location in the raster and click once to begin the tracing process. The Vectorization Trace tool will automatically follow the centerline of the raster cells based on the direction you point the tool's arrow and subsequently generate vector features.

Using raster snapping in conjunction with the Vectorization Trace tool is highly recommended. However, it is not necessary. The Vectorization Trace tool will recognize contiguous raster cells on its own and create features without the use of raster snapping properties. ▶

Tip

Snapping to intersections first

It is recommended that you start creating polygon features at intersections when possible. Since intersections have the highest trace priority, this will ensure that the start and end points share the same coordinates.

1. Click the Editor toolbar and click the Vectorization Trace tool.

2. Snap to a location in the raster layer.

3. Click once to activate the Vectorization Trace tool.

4. Point the tool's arrowhead in the direction you wish to trace. ▶

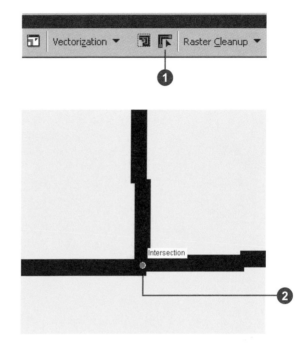

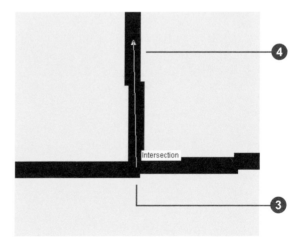

The Vectorization Trace tool works by following along the middle or centerline of a series of connected raster cells. When you click the tool, a cursor will appear that is similar to the standard edit sketch cursor. Once you snap to a location or place your cursor over a raster cell, click once to begin the trace. An arrowhead at the end of the line will appear. Point the arrow in the direction you wish to trace and click once to begin creating features. When creating polygons, the trace tool will create features along the raster lines until it encounters a raster intersection. When this occurs, click to resume the trace. ▶

Tip

Why does the Vectorization Trace tool ignore some raster cells?

Raster cells that are ignored during tracing could be exceeding the maximum raster line width setting. You can change this value via the Vectorization settings dialog box.

See Also

For more information about influencing the output geometry of vector features, see 'An overview of vectorization settings' in this chapter.

5. Click once to start tracing.

   The Vectorization Trace tool will automatically create vertices based on the current vectorization settings.

6. If you encounter an intersection, the Vectorization Trace tool will stop. Point the arrow in the direction you wish to vectorize and click once to continue tracing. ▶

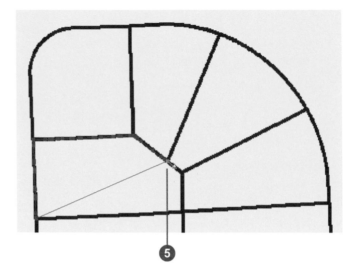

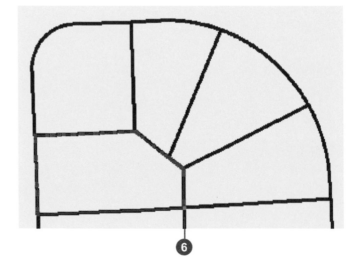

Depending on the current vectorization settings, the location and number of vertices in the line feature will vary. You can change these settings via the Vectorization settings dialog box to improve the outcome of the tracing.

Once you have finished tracing, press F2 to finish the sketch. The next time you save your edits, the polygon feature will be added to the target feature layer.

Tip

Finishing the sketch with the Vectorization Trace tool

Besides pressing the F2 key, you can also double-click to end the sketch. Additionally, you can right-click with the trace tool active to open the tool's context menu and click the Finish Sketch command.

7. When you have reached the start point of the sketch, press F2 to finish the sketch.

A vector polygon feature now represents the connected raster cell area.

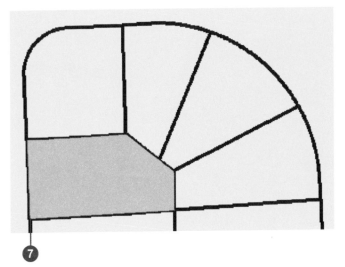

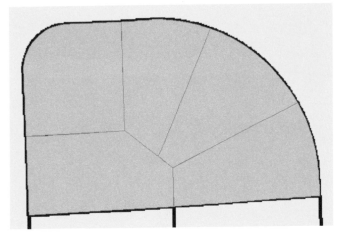

Batch vectorization

5

Batch vectorization is an automated method for converting raster data to vector features. It can encompass vectorizing the entire raster layer or just a portion of it based on a defined area. The batch vectorization process involves other aspects beyond the generation of vector features. These include preparing the raster data, defining the scope of the vectorization, and optimizing the settings that influence the geometric makeup of the output vector features. All of these together comprise batch vectorization.

This chapter will provide an overview of batch vectorization, cover raster selections, discuss raster editing techniques, outline the vectorization settings, and describe how to generate features.

An overview of batch vectorization

Batch vectorization may involve a series of procedures to achieve an acceptable raster-to-vector conversion. Or it can be as simple as executing one command to generate the vector features. Depending on the state of the input raster data you are working with, the vectorization process will vary. This section is intended to provide an overview of the batch vectorization experience.

Raster preprocessing

Raster preprocessing is the practice of preparing your raster data for vectorization. This involves removing noise and raster elements that should not be vectorized. It also involves adding new features or filling holes and gaps to improve the input data, which will ultimately help with the success of the vectorization. ArcScan supports tools to perform these types of operations. These tools can be found in the Raster Cleanup menu and the Raster Painting toolbar. Techniques, such as painting, erasing cells, and exporting to a new raster file, are just a few of the tools ArcScan has to offer.

Defining the scope

The ability to narrow down the scope of the vectorization can help save you time and allow you to be more productive. ArcScan facilitates this process with the support of raster selection tools. These tools allow you to focus on the data that is targeted for the conversion via interactive selections and expression-based queries. You can select a series of connected cells with your cursor or use the Select Connected Cells dialog box to perform a more intelligent selection based on criteria that you specify. You can select cells in either the foreground or background and use a selection as the basis for feature generation. You can also use these tools to assist with the raster cleanup process.

Determining optimal settings

Once you have prepared your raster data for vectorization, the next step is to determine the best settings for the raster-to-vector conversion. Using the right vectorization settings for your data is crucial for ensuring an accurate and successful vectorization. There is no other process in ArcScan that has greater influence in the output vector feature construction. With vectorization settings, you control how intersections will be treated and how many vertices are used to construct a line feature. Additionally, you control how much smoothing should be applied to the lines as well as whether or not to close gaps. Once you have found the optional vectorization settings, you can save them with the map document or export them to an ArcScan style, which can then be reused for similiar data.

Generating features

The final step in the batch vectorization process is the generation of vector features. Since ArcScan supports both centerline and outline vectorization methods, data can be created in line or polygon feature layers. Typically, batch vectorization is performed for the entire raster layer and, therefore, this is the default technique. But ArcScan also supports tools that allow you to vectorize a user-defined portion of the raster. This provides flexibility in cases where you only need to convert a certain area of the raster. You can also take advantage of the cell selection tools and use them in concert with the generate features command to only vectorize the current selected raster cells. ArcScan supports vector data creation for two layer formats: shapefiles and geodatabase feature classes.

An overview of cell selections

The ability to select raster cells can help make the vectorization process more efficient. ArcScan allows for two types of cell selection methods: interactive and expression-based selections. Cell selections support other processes, such as raster cleanup and generating features. This section will provide an overview of cell selections.

Interactive cell selections

The method for interactively selecting raster cells is similar to the way you select vector features in ArcMap. You can click a cell or drag a box around connected cells to select them. Cells that are selected will become highlighted in the current selection color. You can unselect connected cells by holding down the Shift key and clicking them. Or you can use the Clear Selected Cells command to clear the entire selection. You also have the ability to control what you select with the Interactive Selection Target command.

Expression-based cell selection

ArcScan provides more powerful cell selection tools by means of the Select Connected Cells dialog box. This dialog box supports a variety of choices to narrow down your selection criteria. You can select connected cells based on their pixel area or the diagonal of the connected cell's envelope. You can also select cells in the foreground or background or only cells that are in the current extent. In addition to creating new selections, this tool allows you to add to or remove from the current selection.

Using cell selections with other tools

Cell selections are intended to be used with other ArcScan operations. In the raster preprocessing stage, you can use cell selections to assist with your raster cleanup efforts. Commands, such as Erase Selected Cells and Fill Selected Cells, solely rely on a current raster selection. When generating features, you can choose to only vectorize the currently selected cells. Having this functionality can help reduce the time it takes to focus on what needs to be vectorized, which in turn can help increase your productivity.

Saving cell selections

Cell selections can be saved to a new raster file. This is useful when you want to narrow down the number of raster elements in the layer by allowing you to only save what you have selected. ArcScan can save your selected raster data to the following formats: SDE® Raster, ESRI GRID, ERDAS® IMAGINE®, and TIFF.

Interactively selecting connected cells

You can interactively select raster cells using the Select Connected Cells tool. Located on the ArcScan toolbar, this tool allows you to select raster cells using your cursor. You can click on individual cells or drag a box around a group of connected cells to select them.

You can select cells from the foreground or background depending on your current interactive selection target. You can add to the selection by holding down the Shift key and selecting additional cells. Use the Clear Selected Cells command to clear the selection.

Tip
Interactive selection options

Go to the ArcMap Selection Options dialog box to change the interactive selection method. You can choose to select connected cells partially or completely within the box.

Interactively selecting connected cells by single clicking

1. Click the ArcScan toolbar and click the Select Connected Cells tool.

2. Click the connected cells.

   The cells will become highlighted in the current selection color.

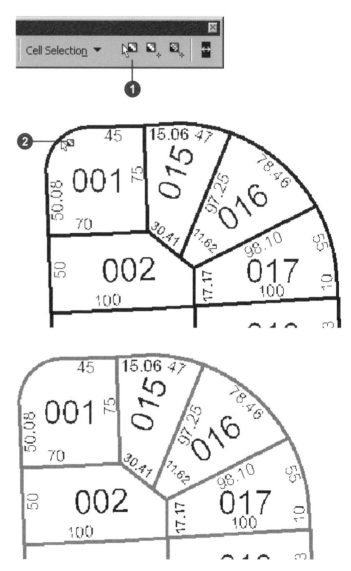

To learn how to change the interactive selection target, see 'Changing the interactive selection target' in this chapter.

Interactively selecting connected cells by dragging a box

1. Click the ArcScan toolbar and click the Select Connected Cells tool.

2. Drag a box around the connected cells.

   The cells will become highlighted in the current selection color. Notice that other cells within the box are also selected.

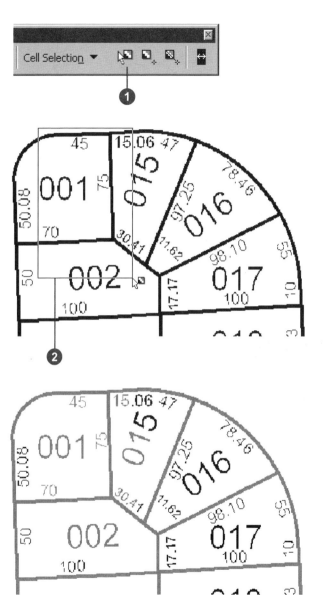

Selecting connected cells by using an expression query

You can select cells by using a query expression in the Select Connected Cells dialog box. This tool offers a more precise way to select cells by allowing you to enter specific information about the raster data to use as selection criteria.

Cells can be selected by their pixel area or the diagonal of their envelope based on a value you enter. You can select cells from the foreground or background and use operators for the query. You can also choose how the selection results will affect the raster (that is, create, add to, remove from).

Tip

Finding holes in rasters

Use small cell area values to locate holes in the raster lines. Once selected, you can use the Fill Selected Cells command to help improve the quality of the lines.

Tip

Selecting only from the current extent

Check the Select only from the current extent box to constrain the cell selection to the current map display.

Opening the Select Connected Cells dialog box

1. Click the Cell Selection menu and click Select Connected Cells.

   The Select connected cells dialog box will appear.

2. Click the dropdown arrow and click a connected cell selection type.

3. Click the dropdown arrow and click where to search for connected cells.

4. Click the dropdown arrow and click an operator to use for the query.

5. Enter the total area or diagonal length in raster pixels to use for the query.

6. Click the dropdown arrow and click how the selection should affect the raster.

7. Check whether or not to only select from the current extent.

8. Click OK.

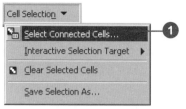

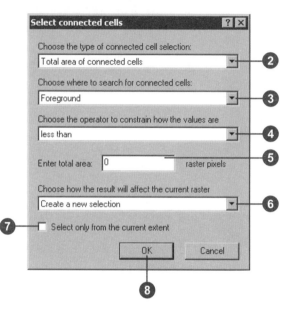

Additional cell selection tools and commands

ArcScan supports additional cell selection tools that help you determine the area and envelope diagonal of cells. This type of information is useful for executing cell selection queries.

The Find Connected Cell Area tool will find the area of the connected cells in pixels. The Find Diagonal of the Envelope of Connected Cells tool will find the diagonal distance from one corner of the cells extent to the other. Both tools will display these respective values when you place your cursor over the connected cells. If you click the connected cells, the Select Connected Cells dialog box will invoke. Depending on the tool you used to select with, the dialog box will appear preset with the selected cells' spatial information. ▶

Finding the connected cell area

1. Click the ArcScan toolbar and click the Find Connected Cell Area tool.

2. Place your cursor over the connected cells to display the total cell area in a Map Tip.

   Click the connected cells to open the Select Connected Cells dialog box, which is preset with the selected cells' spatial information.

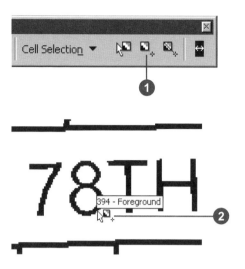

Finding the diagonal of the envelope of connected cells

1. Click the ArcScan toolbar and click the Find Diagonal of the Envelope of Connected Cells tool.

2. Place your cursor over the connected cells to display the envelope's diagonal length in a Map Tip.

   Click the connected cells to open the Select Connected Cells dialog box, which is preset with the selected cells' spatial information.

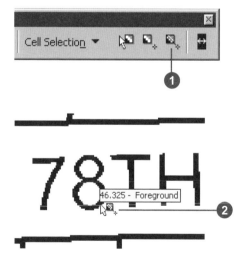

You can choose whether to select cells from the foreground or background with the Interactive Selection Target setting. Cells that exist in the current target color will be available for interactive selection. All other cells will be ignored for interactive selection.

Switching the interactive selection target can be useful during raster editing. It can also help select large portions of the raster's background. ►

Viewing the current interactive selection target

1. Click the Cell Selection menu and click Interactive Selection Target.

   The current interactive selection target will be checked.

Changing the interactive selection target

1. Click the Cell Selection menu and click Interactive Selection Target and click foreground or background cells.

   The Interactive Selection Target submenu will reflect the new setting.

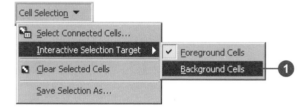

You can unselect all the connected cells that are currently selected by using the Clear Selected Cells command.

You can save the connected cell selection to a new raster file. This allows you to create a new raster that only contains what you have previously selected. ArcScan supports the creation of the following raster formats: SDE Raster, ESRI GRID, ERDAS IMAGINE, and TIFF.

Tip

Other ways to clear selected cells

You can also clear the currently selected cells by clicking on any cell that does not reside in the current interactive selection target color.

See Also

For more information about saving rasters, see 'Saving raster edits to a new file' in this chapter.

Clearing the connected cell selection

1. Click the Cell Selection menu and click Clear Selected Cells.

   All selected connected cells will be unselected.

Saving the raster selection to a new file

1. Click the Cell Selection menu and click Save Selection As.

2. Click the Save as type dropdown arrow and choose a raster format.

3. Navigate to the folder in which you want to save the raster and type a filename.

4. Click Save.

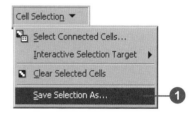

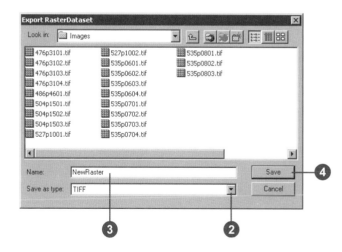

Preparing raster data for vectorization

The effort required to prepare raster data for vectorization will vary from one image to another. In some cases, the input raster may only need minimal changes or none whatsoever. However, there may be instances when you need to perform a fair amount of editing to get the raster in a condition that is viable for conversion. With ArcScan, you can carry out these operations without leaving the ArcMap environment. This section will provide an overview of the ArcScan Raster Cleanup toolset.

The cleanup session

ArcScan employs the notion of a cleanup session similiar to that of the ArcMap edit session. You must start a cleanup session to activate the commands that are available in the Raster Cleanup menu as well as the tools located on the Raster Painting toolbar. All edits made to the raster can only be performed during an active cleanup session. You can stop the cleanup session once you have completed the raster editing tasks. Upon stopping, you will be prompted whether or not to save changes to the raster.

Noise and feature removal

One of the most common tasks performed with the Raster Cleanup tools is the removal of raster cells. This may involve deleting noise or elements that represent information in the raster. Noise may include speckles that result from the scanning process or imperfections in the original source document that were scanned. Features may include cells that represent text, points, lines, and polygons.

There are a few different ways to remove cells from the raster. These include erasing one pixel at a time and erasing a series of connected cells using the Raster Painting toolbar's Erase and Magic Erase tools, respectively. On a broader level, you can use the Erase Selected Cells command to eliminate the currently selected cells. This technique requires the use of the raster selection tools and can really help make the cleanup process more efficient. Whether your raster cleanup requirements are small or large, ArcScan has the tools to help you complete the job.

Adding new cells

You can add new cells to the raster using the tools that are available from the Raster Painting toolbar. You can use the Brush, Fill, and Draw tools for these tasks. The draw tools support four different subtools: line, rectangle, polygon, and ellipse. You can change the size of the brush as well as the width of lines. This allows you to create a variety of geometric shapes in your raster. All of the tools described will create new cells in the current foreground color. However, you can switch the foreground and background colors by clicking the Swap Foreground/Background button on the Raster Painting toolbar. The Raster Painting toolbar's cell creation tools behave much like the tools found in other popular graphics programs. This design allows you to utilize drawing techniques of which you are already familiar.

Saving raster edits

Edits that were performed during the raster cleanup session can be saved directly to the original raster layer. Alternatively, you can also save changes to a new raster file. ArcScan can save your raster to the following formats: SDE Raster, ESRI GRID, ERDAS IMAGINE, and TIFF. This allows you to make all the changes you want without affecting the original source raster. You can save your raster edits during the cleanup session or when you are finished. If you have not saved your edits prior to stopping the cleanup session, you will be prompted to do so at that time. However, you do not have to save changes for them to apply to the vectorization. You can make your changes, vectorize your data, and discard the edits if you desire.

The Raster Cleanup session

To edit your raster layer, you must first start a Raster Cleanup session. Once the cleanup session is started, the Raster Cleanup menu commands will become enabled.

When finished editing your raster layer, you must stop the Raster Cleanup session. This will invoke the Save Raster dialog box, which allows you to choose whether or not you wish to save your raster edits or cancel the Stop Cleanup command. ▶

Tip

Saving raster cleanup edits
You do not have to save raster edits to vectorize the modified raster data. You can discard edits in case you do not wish to change the original raster layer.

Starting a cleanup session

1. Click the Raster Cleanup menu and click Start Cleanup.

Stopping a cleanup session

1. Click the Raster Cleanup menu and click Stop Cleanup.

   The Save Raster dialog box will appear.

2. Click Yes if you want to save your Raster Cleanup edits; click No if you want to discard your edits.

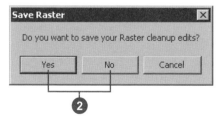

The Raster Cleanup menu supports the Raster Painting Toolbar command. This command will open the Raster Painting toolbar, which provides tools that allow you to interactively perform simple edits on your raster layer. Functions, such as brush, fill, draw, and erase, which are common in many drawing programs, are available from the Raster Painting toolbar. Additional tools that are specific to ArcScan, such as background and foreground color toggle and the Magic Erase tool, are also available.

Opening the Raster Painting toolbar

1. Click the Raster Cleanup menu and click Raster Painting Toolbar.

   The Raster Painting toolbar will appear in the map.

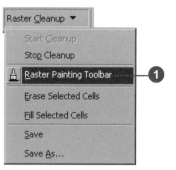

Using the Raster Painting tools

The Raster Painting toolbar supports a variety of tools designed for drawing and erasing raster cells. This section will cover each tool in the order it appears in the toolbar.

The Brush tool allows you to paint. This tool can be used to paint new cells in the raster or add to existing cells in the raster.

You can change the size of the brush by using the Brush Size tool. When you click the Brush Size tool, a dropdown menu displaying four brush size options will appear. The size you choose will become the current brush size. The smallest brush size is one pixel. ▶

Using the Brush tool

1. Click the Raster Painting toolbar and click the Brush tool.

2. Hold down the left mouse button and drag the pointer.

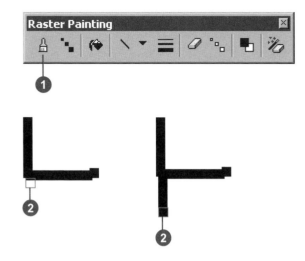

Changing the Brush size

1. Click the Raster Painting toolbar and click the Brush Size button.

2. Choose a new brush size.

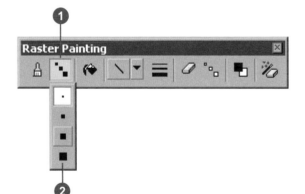

The Fill tool allows you to fill an area or object with the current foreground color. This can help you save time when you need to fill a large area with the foreground color in your raster.

Along with tools to paint and fill cells in your raster, the Raster Painting toolbar also supports tools to draw geometric shapes. The following draw tools are supported: line, rectangle, polygon, and ellipse. You can choose the draw tool by clicking the draw tool dropdown arrow and clicking one of the four draw options. ▶

Tip

Filling multiple cells at one time

You can use the Fill Selected Cells command to fill multiple areas at once. You must have a current raster selection to use this command.

See Also

For more information about selecting raster cells, see 'An overview of cell selections' in this chapter.

See Also

For information about raster snapping, see 'An overview of raster tracing' in Chapter 4, 'Raster tracing'.

Using the Fill tool

1. Click the Raster Painting toolbar and click the Fill tool.

2. Click the area or object you want to fill.

   The area will be filled with the current foreground color.

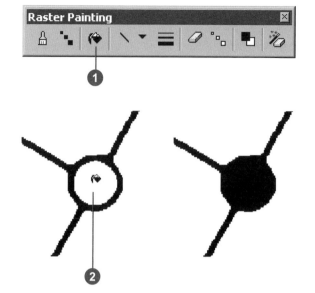

Choosing a draw tool

1. Click the Raster Painting toolbar and click the Draw tool dropdown arrow.

2. Choose a draw tool from the menu.

   This will now become the active draw tool.

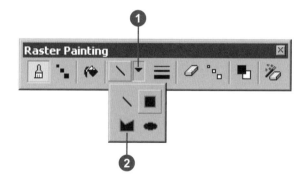

You can draw two-point lines or multiple-point lines with the Line Draw tool. To draw a two-point line, left-click to start drawing the line and double-click at the end location to finish the line. To draw multiple-point lines, left-click to start drawing the line and left-click again to create a vertex. Repeat these steps until you have reached the endpoint location. Double-click to finish the line.

You can change the width of the line by using the Line Width tool. When you click the Line Width tool, a dropdown menu displaying four line width options will appear. The line width you choose will become the current line width. ▶

Drawing lines

1. Click the Raster Painting toolbar and click the Line tool.

2. Left-click to start drawing the line.

3. Click locations where you want to create a vertex.

4. Double-click to finish drawing the line.

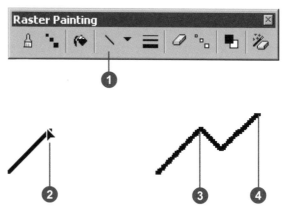

Changing the line width

1. Click the Raster Painting toolbar and click the Line Width button.

2. Choose a line width option from the menu.

   This will now become the current line width.

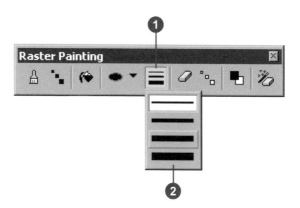

You can draw rectangular shapes with the Rectangle draw tool. To draw a rectangle, click the left mouse button and drag a box that defines the extents of the rectangle while holding down the button. Release the left mouse button to create the rectangle.

You can create multiple-sided polygon shapes with the Polygon draw tool. To draw a polygon, click with the left mouse button, point in the direction you wish to draw, and click again to create a corner of the polygon. When you have finished creating all of the corners of the polygon, double-click to finish the drawing. ▶

Drawing rectangles

1. Click the Raster Painting toolbar and click the Rectangle tool.

2. Left-click to start drawing the rectangle.

3. Drag a box to define the extents of the rectangle.

4. Release the left mouse button to finish the drawing.

   The rectangle will be filled with the current foreground color.

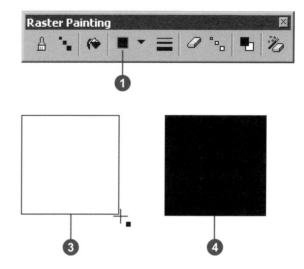

Drawing polygons

1. Click the Raster Painting toolbar and click the Polygon tool.

2. Left-click to start drawing the polygon.

3. Click to create a corner of the polygon.

4. Double-click to finish the drawing.

   The polygon will be filled with the current foreground color.

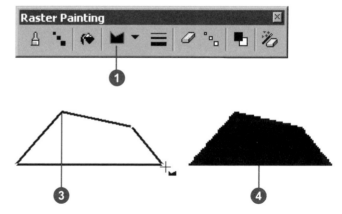

You can draw elliptical shapes with the Ellipse draw tool. To draw an ellipse, click the left mouse button and drag a box that defines the extents of the ellipse while holding down the button. Release the left mouse button to create the ellipse.

You can delete cells in the raster with the Erase tool. You can erase small areas in the raster by clicking once with the tool. You can erase larger areas in the raster by clicking and holding the left mouse button and dragging the erase cursor over a series of raster cells. ▶

Tip

The Erase tool will honor the current raster snapping settings

You can snap to rasters with the Erase tool to help you accurately delete cells. The Erase tool will use the current raster snapping properties that are set in the Snapping Environment window.

Tip

Using the spacebar to suspend snapping

In cases in which you want to temporarily suspend snapping, hold down the spacebar while positioning the cursor in the desired location.

Drawing ellipses

1. Click the Raster Painting toolbar and click the Ellipse tool.

2. Left-click to start drawing the ellipse.

3. Drag a box to define the extents of the ellipse.

4. Release the left mouse button to finish the drawing.

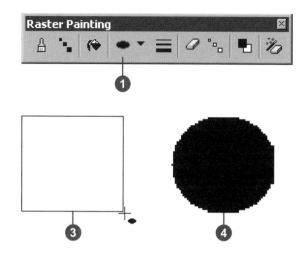

Using the Erase tool

1. Click the Raster Painting toolbar and click the Erase tool.

2. Left-click to start erasing cells.

3. Hold down the left mouse button and drag the Erase tool over the raster cells.

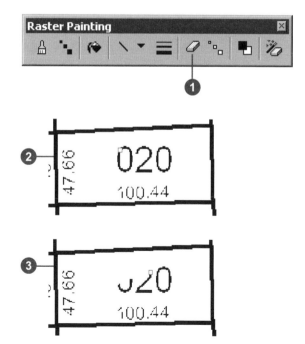

You can change the size of the Erase tool by using the Erase Size tool. When you click the Erase Size tool, a dropdown menu displaying four erase size options will appear. The size you choose will become the current erase size.

The foreground and background colors are displayed on the Raster Painting toolbar with the foreground color always on top. You can switch the foreground and background colors with the Swap Foreground/Background tool. Since the draw tools only create cells in the foreground, switching colors allows you to use them for erasing purposes or to overwrite cells. Consequently, the Erase tool will assume brush-like characteristics since it will now be painting cells in the foreground instead of the background, which is the default. ▶

Changing the Erase tool size

1. Click the Raster Painting toolbar and click the Brush Size button.

2. Choose a new brush size.

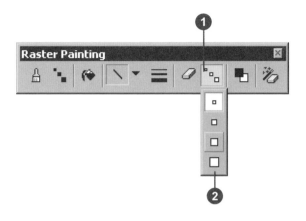

Switching the foreground and background colors

1. Click the Raster Painting toolbar and click the Swap Foreground/Background tool.

   The foreground and background colors are now reversed. The Swap Foreground/Background button icon will reflect the new setting.

In addition to the standard Erase tool, the Raster Painting toolbar supports a more robust tool for removing a large number of raster cells at one time. This tool is called the Magic Erase tool. It allows you to erase connected cells. You can click once on the connected cells, and they will be erased. This includes the connected cells that are beyond the current map display extents. You can also drag a box around a series of connected cells to erase them. All connected cells that are completely within the box will be removed. Connected cells that pass through the dragged box will not be affected.

Using the Magic Erase tool is an efficient way to remove a large number of cells with minimal effort. It is useful for erasing noise and text without having to worry about deleting raster cells that you want to vectorize.

Using the Magic Erase tool by single-clicking

1. Click the Raster Painting toolbar and click the Magic Erase tool.

2. Click the connected cells.

   The cells are now erased.

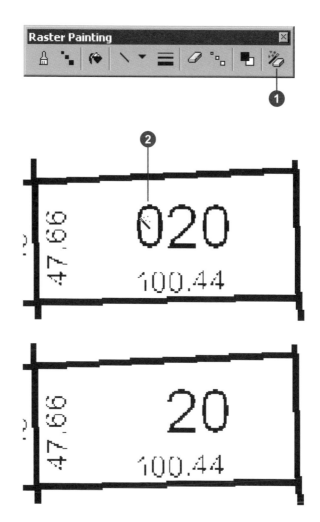

Using the Magic Erase tool by dragging a box

1. Click the Raster Painting toolbar and click the Magic Erase tool.

2. Drag a box around the connected cells.

3. Release the left mouse button.

   The cells are now erased. All connected cells that extend beyond the dragged box are not erased.

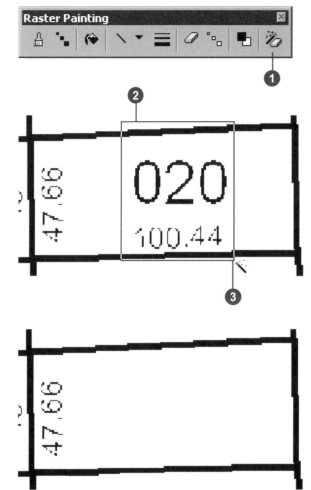

Using the Raster Cleanup commands

Two of the Raster Cleanup commands rely on a current raster selection. These are the Erase Selected Cells and Fill Selected Cells commands.

The Erase Selected cells command will delete any cell that is part of a raster selection. This can help you save time by reducing the amount of interactive editing required to eliminate unwanted cells. When used in conjunction with an expression-based query, this command can be an efficient way to remove data from the raster on a broad scale.

The Fill Selected Cells command will fill or paint any cell that is part of a raster selection. This can be useful for filling holes that may exist in the raster lines that could impede the vectorization. When used in conjunction with an expression-based query, this command can be an efficient way to clean up your data. ▶

Erasing selected cells

1. Click the Raster Cleanup menu and click Erase Selected Cells.

   All the selected cells are erased.

Filling selected cells

1. Click the Raster Cleanup menu and click Fill Selected Cells.

   All the selected cells are filled with the foreground color.

You can save your raster edits any time during the raster cleanup session or when you stop the cleanup session. When you use the Save command, edits will be written to the target raster layer.

When you use the Save As command, the edits along with the entire raster will be written to a new raster file. This option is recommended for those who do not wish to modify the original raster layer. ArcScan supports the creation of the following raster formats: SDE Raster, ESRI GRID, ERDAS IMAGINE, and TIFF.

You do not have to save edits to vectorize the data. You can start a cleanup session, modify the raster, and vectorize the data without ever saving the raster edits. When prompted to save edits, choose No to discard the changes.

Tip

SDE Rasters cannot be edited

SDE Rasters cannot be edited with the Raster Cleanup tools. If you need to edit an SDE Raster, you should save it to an editable raster format.

Saving raster edits

1. Click the Raster Cleanup menu and click Save.

Saving raster edits to a new file

1. Click the Raster Cleanup menu and click Save As.

2. Click the Save as type dropdown arrow and choose a raster format.

3. Navigate to the folder in which you want to save the raster and type a filename.

4. Click Save.

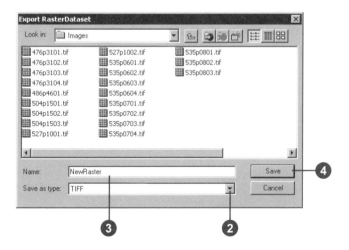

Applying the vectorization settings for batch vectorization

Batch vectorization is most affected by the vectorization settings that you apply. In the following pages you will see the steps to take to apply each of these settings.

Tip

A modeless Vectorization Settings dialog box

The modeless design of the Vectorization Settings dialog box allows you to continually update the settings and apply the changes without having to reopen it.

See Also

For more information about vectorization settings, see 'An overview of the vectorization settings' in Chapter 4, 'Raster tracing'.

Choosing an intersection solution

1. Click the Vectorization menu and click Vectorization Settings.

2. Click the Intersection Solution dropdown arrow and choose the Geometrical, Median, or None option.

3. Click Apply.

4. Click Close.

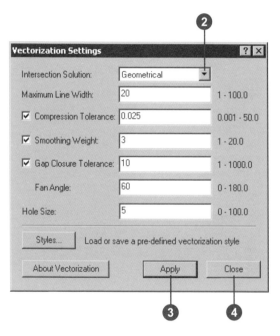

Specifying the maximum line width

1. Click the Vectorization menu and click Vectorization Settings.

2. Enter a value for the maximum line width.

3. Click Apply.

4. Click Close.

Setting the compression tolerance

1. Click the Vectorization menu and click Vectorization Settings.

2. Check the Compression Tolerance check box.

3. Enter a value for the compression tolerance.

4. Click Apply.

5. Click Close.

Setting the smoothing weight

1. Click the Vectorization menu and click Vectorization Settings.

2. Check the Smoothing Weight check box.

3. Enter a value for the smoothing weight.

4. Click Apply.

5. Click Close.

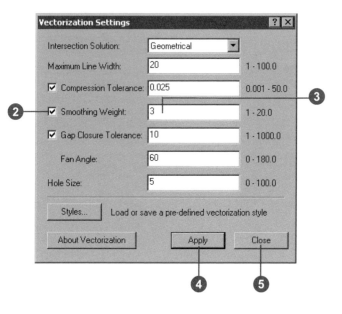

Setting the gap closure tolerance and fan angle

1. Click the Vectorization menu and click Vectorization Settings.

2. Check the Gap Closure Tolerance check box.

3. Enter a gap closure tolerance.

4. Enter a fan angle.

5. Click Apply.

6. Click Close.

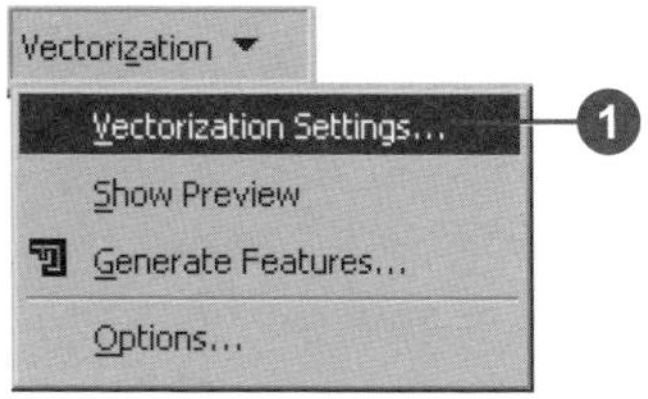

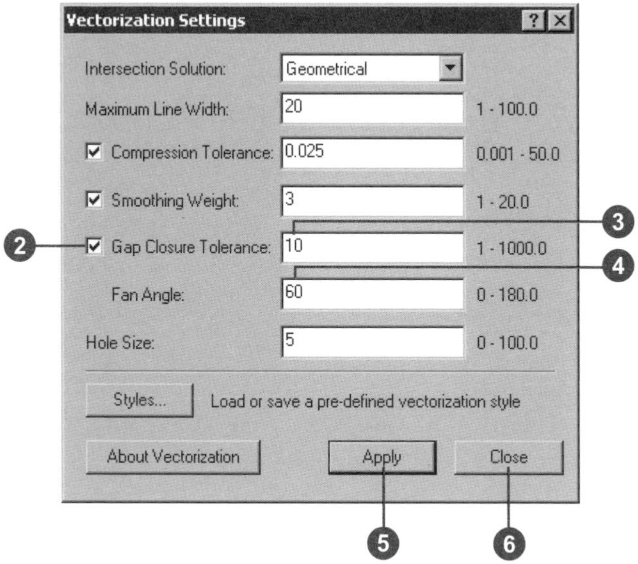

Vectorization ▼

1

Vectorization Settings...
Show Preview
Generate Features...
Options...

Vectorization Settings ? X

Intersection Solution:	Geometrical ▼	
Maximum Line Width:	20	1 - 100.0
☑ Compression Tolerance:	0.025	0.001 - 50.0
☑ Smoothing Weight:	3	1 - 20.0
☑ Gap Closure Tolerance:	10	1 - 1000.0
Fan Angle:	60	0 - 180.0
Hole Size:	5	0 - 100.0

2 **3** **4**

Styles...   Load or save a pre-defined vectorization style

About Vectorization   Apply   Close

5 **6**

Saving a vectorization style

1. Click the Vectorization menu and click Vectorization Settings.

2. Click the Styles button.

   The Vectorization Settings Style dialog box will appear.

3. Click the Save button.

4. Type a name for the new vectorization style and click OK.

5. Click OK.

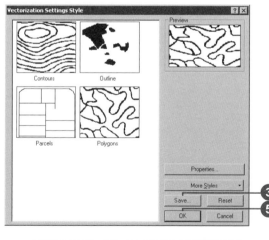

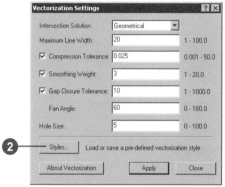

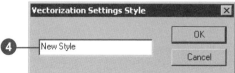

Retaining vectorization settings

You can retain your vectorization settings by saving the map document.

Loading a vectorization style

1. Click the Vectorization menu and click Vectorization Settings.

2. Click the Styles button.

   The Vectorization Settings Style dialog box will appear.

3. Click the More Styles button and choose a style in the menu or click Add to browse for a style.

4. Click OK.

   The vectorization settings will reflect the loaded style.

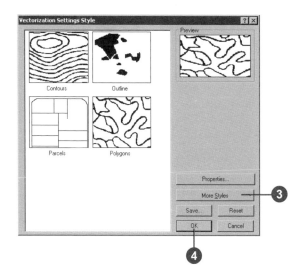

Previewing the vectorization

ArcScan allows you to preview the vectorization prior to generating features. This functionality provides a way for you to test the vectorization settings and view the results without having to create features, which can help save you time.

When the Show Preview command is checked, preview features will continue to be displayed after you zoom or pan. You can change the preview symbology in the Vectorization Options dialog box.

Tip

Updating the preview after changing vectorization settings

When you modify the vectorization settings, you update the preview display to changes by clicking the Apply button in the Vectorization Settings dialog box.

See Also

For more information about changing the preview symbology, see 'Changing the preview symbols' in Chapter 3, 'ArcScan basics'.

Using the Show Preview command

1. Click the Vectorization menu and click Show Preview.

   A check mark will indicate if the Show Preview command is active.

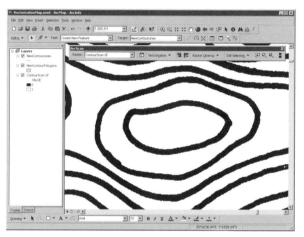

Map prior to previewing the vectorization.

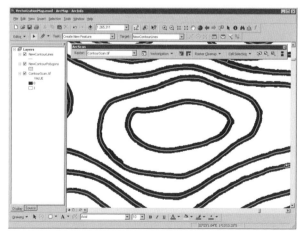

Map with Show Preview enabled.

Generating features

Once you have determined the best possible settings for the vectorization, it is time to create the vector features. You can create features by using the Generate Features command. This command will open the Generate Features dialog box, which allows you to choose the target line and polygon layers. There is also an option to generate features for the currently selected cells only and whether or not to have the new features selected after they are generated.

When using the centerline vectorization method, the Generate Features dialog box will require that the target line layer be chosen. Generating polygons in cases where the maximum line width is exceeded is optional. You can also choose to save the average width of each line feature to an existing field in the target line layer. ▶

Tip

How do I change the vectorization method?

You can change the vectorization method in the Vectorization Options dialog box. The supported methods are centerline and outline.

Generating features using the centerline vectorization method

1. Click the Vectorization menu and click Generate Features.

   The Generate Features dialog box will appear.

2. Click the dropdown arrow and click the line layer in which to add the centerlines.

3. Check whether or not to save the average width of each line feature to an existing field.

4. Click the dropdown arrow and click to which field to save the average width of each line feature.

5. Check whether or not to generate polygons where the maximum line width setting is exceeded.

6. Click the dropdown arrow and click the polygon layer in which to add the polygons.

7. Check whether or not to generate features for currently selected cells only.

8. Check whether or not to have new features selected after their creation.

9. Click OK.

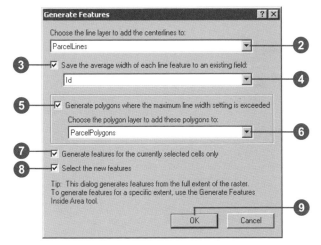

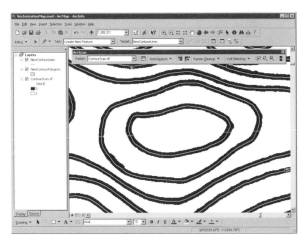

Map showing generated features.

When using the outline
vectorization method, the
Generate Features dialog box
will require that the target
polygon layer be chosen.
Generating lines in cases where
the maximum number of vertices
in a polygon is exceeded is
optional. ►

Tip

Generating polygons from lines

You can use the Construct Features command to create polygons from lines that were generated with a centerline vectorization. The Construct Features command is located on the Topology toolbar.

Tip

Changing the maximum number of vertices in a polygon

You can change the maximum number of vertices in a polygon in the Vectorization Options dialog box. Click the Advanced button to access this setting.

Generating features using the outline vectorization method

1. Click the Vectorization menu and click Generate Features.

   The Generate Features dialog box will appear.

2. Click the dropdown arrow and click the polygon layer in which to add the outlines.

3. Click the dropdown arrow and click a line layer to add lines to in cases where the maximum number of vertices in a polygon is exceeded.

4. Check whether or not to generate features for currently selected cells only.

5. Check whether or not to have new features selected after their creation.

6. Click OK.

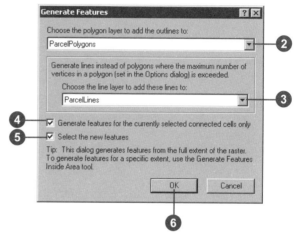

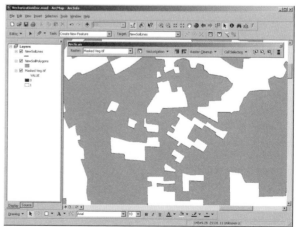

You can batch vectorize a subset of the raster layer by using the Generate Features Inside Area tool. This tool allows you to interactively draw a polygon shape on the map that will be used to define the area for which all cells inside it will be vectorized. When you have completed defining this area with the cursor, double-click to finish the drawing. This will display the Generate Features dialog box. The contents of the Generate Features dialog box will reflect the current vectorization method.

The Generate Features Inside Area tool is useful when you only want to vectorize a certain portion of the raster. All of the options provided by the Generate Features command are also available when using this tool.

Tip

Snapping to rasters

You can snap to rasters when you use the Generate Features Inside Area tool to draw a polygon. This can help you create the area of interest more accurately.

See Also

For more information about generating outline features, see 'Generating features using the outline vectorization method' in this chapter.

Generating features inside a defined area

1. Click the ArcScan toolbar and click the Generate Features Inside Area tool.

2. Left-click to start drawing the polygon. Create a corner with each additional click.

3. Double-click to finish the drawing.

4. Click the dropdown arrow and click the line layer in which to add the centerlines.

5. Check whether or not to save the average width of each line feature to an existing field.

6. Click the dropdown arrow and click the field in which to save the average width of each line feature.

7. Check whether or not to generate polygons where the maximum line width setting is exceeded.

8. Click the dropdown arrow and click the polygon layer in which to add the polygons.

9. Check whether or not to generate features for currently selected cells only.

10. Check whether or not to have new features selected after their creation.

11. Click OK.

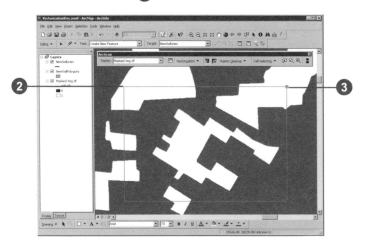

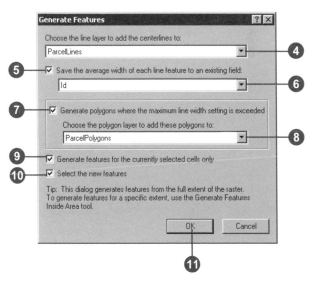

Appendix

This appendix provides information about the performance of ArcScan processes with various types of raster datasets and settings. This information is intended to be used as a reference for operations that impact system performance, such as cell selections and vector feature generation. Each performance analysis includes data about the size of the raster dataset, memory usage, and the time it took to complete a particular task.

A performance comparison of ArcScan processes

Map type	Rows	Columns	At rest	Small select	Large select	Large select dialog	Generate features
Parcel	10,400	14,800	255	10	20	20	30
Contour	38,000	36,000	260	10	30	150	100
Veg Poly	20,000	18,000	255	10	50	50	90
Drainage	11,050	10,500	255	5	5	10	10
Veg Mask	23,000	18,000	255	0	0	20	20
Nav Chart	18,400	25,600	255	10	80	120	380
Nav Chart	18,400	25,600	280	10	80	120	890
DNC	27,000	18,000	265	5	35	60	180

Notes:

At rest: Base memory with document loaded

Small select: Memory used to interactively select a small number of connected cells

Large select: Memory used to interactively select a large number of connected cells

Large select dialog: Memory used to select a large number of connected cells via the Select Connected Cells dialog box

Generate features: Memory used to vectorize features

Data Sources:

Parcel: Medium density parcel map lines

Contour: Light-to-medium density contour map

Veg Poly: Medium density vegetation map polygons

Drainage: Light density drainage map lines

Veg Mask: Large vegetation mask polygons

Nav Chart: Navigation Chart—San Diego

DNC: Digital Nautical Chart

Int. solution	Line width	Compression	Smoothing	Number of features	Time (min.)
Geom	20	0.025	3	4,652	2
None	20	0.25	3	3,453	4
Geom	10	0.25	3	9,714	2
Geom	15	0.25	3	1,200	1
None	20	1	2	214	2
Geom	20	0.025	3	70,000	10
Geom	2	0.025	3	50,000	10
Geom	20	0.025	3	30,000	6

Glossary

analysis

The process of identifying a question or issue to be addressed, modeling the issue, investigating model results, interpreting the results, and possibly making a recommendation.

area

1. The planimetric view of a polygon feature or surface.

2. The surface area of a three-dimensional surface or of the portion of a surface above or below a reference plane. Surface is measured along the slope of a surface and is always greater than the two-dimensional planimetric extent of the surface. When compared to planimetric area, surface area gives you an idea of the surface roughness.

attribute

1. A piece of information describing a map feature. The attributes of a census tract, for example, might include its area, population, and average per capita income.

2. A characteristic of a geographic feature described by numbers, characters, images, and CAD drawings, typically stored in tabular format and linked to the feature by a user-assigned identifier. For example, the attributes of a well might include depth and gallons per minute.

3. A column in a table.

background

1. You can set the color of the background of a scene to suggest sky, empty space, or any color that suits your visualization purpose. The default background color is white.

2. Some rasters (typically images) have border areas that are outside of the area for which image data was collected. This area is often assigned an arbitrary value (often black, or 255). You can control the display of these parts of a raster by setting the background color on the Symbology tab of the Layer Properties dialog box. See also NoData.

band

A measure of a characteristic or quality of the features observed in a raster. Some rasters have a single band; others have more than one. For example, satellite imagery commonly has multiple bands representing different wavelengths of energy along the electromagnetic spectrum.

batch vectorization

An automated process that converts raster data into vector features for the entire raster or a portion of it based on user-defined settings.

button

A command that runs a macro or custom code when clicked. Buttons can be added to any menu or toolbar. When they appear in a menu, buttons are referred to as menu commands.

cell

Also known as a pixel, raster cell, or grid cell. A discretely uniform unit, such as a square or rectangle, that represents a portion of the earth, such as a square meter or square mile. Each grid cell has a value that corresponds to the feature or characteristic at that site, such as a soil type, census tract, or vegetation class.

cell selection

The process of selecting connected cells either interactively or by using a SQL-based query expression.

cell size

The length in map units of the side of a cell of a raster. The cell size is the same in both the x and y directions.

centerline vectorization

A vectorization method that generates vector features along the center of connected cells. It is typically used for vectorizing parcel and survey scanned maps.

classify

The process of sorting or arranging attribute values into groups or categories; all members of a group are represented on the map by the same symbol.

column

The vertical dimension of a table. A column has a name and a data type applied to all values in the column. See also attribute and field.

control points

Points you establish on a paper map whose coordinates represent known ground points or specific locations. Control points are used to register a paper map before you begin digitizing features on it using a digitizer.

coordinate

A set of numbers that designate location in a given reference system, such as x,y in a planar coordinate system or x,y,z in a three-dimensional coordinate system. Coordinate pairs represent a location on the earth's surface relative to other locations. See also vector.

coordinate system

1. A reference system used to measure horizontal and vertical distances on a planimetric map. A coordinate system is usually defined by a map projection, a spheroid of reference, a datum, one or more standard parallels, a central meridian, and possible shifts in the x- and y-directions to locate x,y positions of point, line, and area features.

2. In ArcInfo, a system with units and characteristics defined by a map projection. A common coordinate system is used to spatially register geographic data for a given area.

3. A reference system consisting of a set of points, lines, and/or surfaces and a set of rules used to define the positions of points in space either in two or three dimensions.

data frame

In ArcMap, a frame on the map that displays layers occupying the same geographic area. You may have one or more data frames on your map depending on how you want to organize your data. For instance, one data frame might highlight a study area, and another might provide an overview of where the study area is located.

data type

The attribute of a variable or field (column) that determines the kind of data it can store. Common data types are character, integer, decimal, single, double, and string.

data view

An all-purpose view in ArcMap and ArcReader for exploring, displaying, and querying geographic data. This view hides all map elements, such as title, North arrows, and scalebars. See also layout view.

dataset

1. Any feature class, table, or collection of feature classes or tables in the geodatabase.

2. A named collection of logically related data items arranged in a prescribed manner.

digitizing

1. To encode geographic features in digital form as x,y coordinates.

2. The process of converting the features on a paper map into digital format. When you digitize a map, you use a digitizing tablet, or digitizer, which is connected to your computer. You then trace over features with a digitizer puck, which is similar to a mouse. The x,y coordinates of these features are automatically recorded and stored as spatial data.

3. Heads-up digitizing features from onscreen data (e.g., rasters).

edit cache

A setting used in spatial data editing in ArcMap that causes the features visible in the current map extent to be held in memory on your local machine. Designed to be used when working with large amounts of data, an edit cache results in faster editing because ArcMap doesn't have to retrieve the data from the server.

edit session

In ArcMap, all editing takes place within an edit session. An edit session begins when you choose Start Editing from the Editor menu and ends when you choose Stop Editing.

Editor toolbar

A set of tools that allows you to create and modify features and their attributes in ArcMap.

ellipse

A geometric shape equivalent to a circle that is viewed obliquely; a flattened circle.

extent

The coordinate pairs defining the minimum bounding rectangle (xmin, ymin and xmax, ymax) of a data source. All coordinates for the data source fall within this boundary.

feature

1. An object class in a geodatabase that has a field of type geometry. Features are stored in feature classes.

2. A representation of a real-world object.

3. A point, line, or polygon in a coverage, shapefile, or geodatabase feature class.

feature class

1. A classification describing the format of geographic features and supporting data in a coverage. Coverage feature classes for representing geographic features include point, arc, node, route-system, route, section, polygon, and region. One or more coverage features are used to model geographic features; for example, arcs and nodes can be used to model linear features, such as street centerlines. The tic, annotation, link, and boundary feature classes provide supporting data for coverage data management and viewing.

2. The conceptual representation of a geographic feature. When referring to geographic features, feature classes include point, line, area, and surface. In a geodatabase, an object class that stores features and has a field of type geometry in a geodatabase.

field

A column in a table. Each field contains the values for a single attribute.

foreground

Area in a raster layer where cells are eligible for selection and vectorization.

format

The pattern into which data is systematically arranged for use on a computer. A file format is the specific design of how information is organized in the file. For example, raster datasets come in different formats, such as ESRI grid, TIFF, and MrSID™ from LizardTech Software.

geodatabase

An object-oriented geographic database that provides services for managing geographic data. These services include validation rules, relationships, and topological associations. A geodatabase contains feature datasets and is hosted inside a relational database management system.

geometric transformation

The process of rectifying a raster dataset to map coordinates or converting a raster dataset from one project to another.

georeferencing

The process of defining how raster data is situated in map coordinates. Georeferencing raster data allows it to be viewed, queried, and analyzed with other geographic data.

grid

A geographic representation of the world as an array of equally sized square cells arranged in rows and columns. Each grid cell is referenced by its geographic x,y location. See raster.

holes

Small gaps in a raster line that are completely surrounded by foreground pixels. Holes may be caused by the poor quality of the source document or scanning process.

image

Represents geographic features by dividing the world into discrete squares called cells. Examples include satellite and aerial photographs, scanned documents, and building photographs. See also raster.

interactive vectorization

A manual process for converting raster data into vector features that involves tracing raster cells.

layer

A collection of similar geographic features—such as rivers, lakes, counties, or cities—in a particular area or place referenced together for display on a map. A layer references geographic data stored in a data source, such as a coverage, and defines how to display it. You can create and manage layers as you would any other type of data in your database.

layout view

The view for laying out your map in ArcMap and ArcReader. Layout view shows the virtual page on which you place and arrange geographic data and map elements—such as titles, legends, and scalebars—for printing. See also data view.

map

1. A graphical representation of geographic information. It includes geographic data and other elements, such as a title, North arrow, legend, and scalebar. You can interactively display and query the geographic data on a map and prepare a printable map by arranging the map elements around the data in a visually pleasing manner.

2. The document used in ArcMap to display and work with geographic data. A map contains one or more layers of geographic data and various supporting map elements, such as a scalebar. Layers on a map are contained in data frames.

map document

In ArcMap, the disk-based representation of a map. Map documents can be printed or embedded in other documents. Map documents have a .mxd file extension.

map projection

See projection.

NoData

Some rasters have empty cells within the area for which data was collected. For grids, these cells are NoData, while for other formats they are often assigned a special value, such as -9999. Rasters with some NoData cells are also created by some raster analysis tools, or the Spatial Analyst Reclassify function. You can control the display of NoData by setting the NoData color on the Symbology tab of the Layer Properties dialog box. See background and null value.

noise

Irrelevant or meaningless cells that exist in rasters due to poor scanning or imperfections in the original source document.

null value

The absence of a value. A geographic feature for which there is no associated attribute information.

outline vectorization

A vectorization method that generates vector features along the border of connected cells. It is typically used for vectorizing land use and vegetation scanned maps.

pixel

See cell.

point

A single x,y coordinate pair that represents a single geographic feature, such as a telephone pole.

polygon

A two-dimensional feature representing an area, such as a state or county.

projection

A mathematical formula that transforms feature locations between the earth's curved surface and a map's flat surface. A projected coordinate system includes the information needed to transform locations expressed as latitude and longitude values to x,y coordinates. Projections cause distortions in one or more of these spatial properties: distance, area, shape, and direction.

query

A question or request used for selecting features. A query often appears in the form of a statement or logical expression. In ArcMap, a query contains a field, an operator, and a value.

raster

Represents any data source that uses a grid structure to store geographic information (e.g., images and grids).

raster cleanup

The process of drawing, filling, and erasing raster cells using ArcScan Raster Cleanup and Raster Painting tools.

raster dataset

Contains raster data organized into bands. Each band consists of an array of cells with optional attributes for each cell, or pixel. Raster datasets come in many different formats. See format.

raster intersection

Three or more raster linear elements that meet at a common point.

raster postprocessing

The automatic correction of vector feature results by ArcScan immediately after batch vectorization is completed. Postprocessing involves generalizing and smoothing lines and straightening angles.

raster preprocessing

Simple raster editing you should do to prepare your images for vectorization. Preprocessing includes image clipping, image positioning, image resizing, image flipping or mirror rotating, and image deskewing.

raster snapping

The process of moving a feature to coincide with the location of connected cells within a specified snapping distance or tolerance. Raster snapping is typically used to assist with tracing raster data.

raster tracing

An interactive vectorization process that involves drawing along the centerline of connected raster cells in the map to create vector features.

relationship

An association or link between two objects in a database. Relationships can exist between spatial objects (features in feature classes), nonspatial objects (rows in a table), or between spatial and nonspatial objects.

row

1. A record in an attribute table.

2. The horizontal dimension of a table composed of a set of columns containing one data item each.

3. A horizontal group of cells in a raster.

select

To choose from a number or group of features or records; to create a separate set or subset.

Select connected cells dialog box

A tool that allows you to perform complex cell selection based on pixel areas and envelope extents using SQL expressions.

shape

The characteristic appearance or visible form of a geographic object. Geographic objects can be represented on a map using one of three basic shapes: points, lines, or polygons.

shapefile

A vector data storage format for storing the location, shape, and attributes of geographic features. A shapefile is stored in a set of related files and contains one feature class.

sketch

When editing in ArcMap, a shape that represents a feature's geometry. Every existing feature on a map has this alternate form, a sketch. A sketch lets you see exactly how a feature is composed with all vertices and segments of the feature visible. To modify a feature, you must modify its sketch. To create a feature, you must first create a sketch. You can only create line and polygon sketches, as points have neither vertices nor segments.

Sketches help complete the current task. For example, the Create New Feature task uses a sketch you create to make a new feature. The Extend/Trim Feature task uses a sketch you create to determine where the selected feature will be extended or trimmed. The Cut Polygon Feature task uses a sketch you create to determine where the polygon will be cut into two features.

snapping

The process of moving a feature to coincide with the coordinates of another feature within a specified snapping distance or tolerance.

snapping environment

Settings in the ArcMap Snapping Environment window and Editing Options dialog box that help you establish exact locations in relation to other features. You determine the snapping environment by setting the snapping tolerance, snapping properties, and snapping priority.

snapping priority

During ArcMap editing, the order in which snapping will occur by layer. You can set the snapping priority by dragging the layer names in the Snapping Environment window to new locations.

snapping properties

You can choose the part of a feature, vertex, edge, or endpoint to which you want a new feature to snap (precisely connect) by setting the layer snapping properties in the ArcMap editing environment. For example, you can set the snapping properties so that the endpoint of a new feature will snap to the vertex of an existing feature. When the pointer comes within the snapping tolerance of the vertex, the endpoint of the new feature snaps to the vertex of the existing feature.

snapping tolerance

During ArcMap editing, the distance within which the pointer or a feature will snap to another location. If the location being snapped to, such as a vertex, boundary, midpoint, or connection, is within the distance you set, the pointer will automatically snap. For example, if you want to snap a power line to a utility pole and the snapping tolerance is set to 25 pixels, whenever the power line comes within a 25-pixel range of the pole, it will automatically snap to it. Snapping tolerance can be measured using either map units or pixels.

SQL

Structured Query Language. A syntax for defining and manipulating data from a relational database. Developed by IBM in the 1970s, it has become an industry standard for query languages in most relational database management systems.

stream tolerance

The interval at which vertices are added along the feature you're digitizing in stream mode. When streaming, vertices are automatically created at a defined interval as you move the mouse. For example, if the stream tolerance is set to 10 map units, you must move the pointer at least 10 map units before the next vertex will be created. If you move the pointer more than 10 map units, there may be more space between vertices, but there will always be a minimum interval of 10 map units. Stream tolerance is measured in map units.

styles

Files that contain batch vectorization setting information that influences how the output vector features are generated.

symbol

A graphic pattern used to represent a feature. For example, line symbols represent arc features; marker symbols, points; shade symbols, polygons; and text symbols, annotation. Many characteristics define symbols, including color, size, angle, and pattern.

symbology

The criteria used to determine symbols for the features in a layer. A characteristic of a feature may influence the size, color, and shape of the symbol used.

table

A set of data elements that has a horizontal dimension (rows) and a vertical dimension (columns). See also attribute table.

table of contents

In ArcMap, the table of contents lists all the data frames and layers on the map and shows what features the symbols in each layer represent. ArcScene also has a table of contents.

target layer

Used in ArcMap editing, a setting in the Target Layer dropdown list that determines the layer to which new features will be added. The target layer is set by clicking a layer in the Target Layer dropdown list. For instance, if you set the target layer to Buildings, any features you create will be part of the Buildings layer. You must set the target layer whenever you're creating new features—whether you're creating them with the Sketch tool, by copying and pasting, or by buffering another feature.

tolerance

A coverage has many processing tolerances (fuzzy, tic match, dangle length) and editing tolerances (weed, grain, edit distance, snap distance, and nodesnap distance). Stored in a TOL file, ArcInfo uses the tolerance values as defaults in many automation, editing, and processing operations. You can edit a coverage's tolerances using its Properties dialog box in ArcCatalog.

topology

1. In geodatabases, relationships between connected features in a geometric network or shared borders between features in a planar topology.

2. In coverages, the spatial relationships between connecting or adjacent features (for example, arcs, nodes, polygons, and points). The topology of an arc includes its from- and to-nodes and its left and right polygons. Topological relationships are built from simple elements into complex elements: points (simplest elements), arcs (sets of connected points), areas (sets of connected arcs), and routes (sets of sections, which are arcs or portions of arcs). Redundant data (coordinates) is eliminated because an arc may represent a linear feature, part of the boundary of an area feature, or both.

vector

A coordinate-based data structure commonly used to represent linear geographic features. Each linear feature is represented as an ordered list of vertices. Traditional vector data structures include double-digitized polygons and arc–node models. Coverages and shapefiles are examples of vectors.

vectorization

The conversion of raster data to vector features.

vectorization settings

Settings that control which raster cells are eligible for vectorization; influences how the geometry of the output vector data is constructed during vectorization.

Vectorization Trace tool

Allows you to manually trace raster cells and generate features for raster data that you wish to vectorize.

vertex

A point that joins two segments of a feature. For instance, a square building would have four vertices, one at each corner.

workspace

A container for file-based geographic data. This can be a folder that contains shapefiles, an ArcInfo workspace that contains coverages, a personal geodatabase, or an ArcSDE database connection.

Index

A

Advanced editing 38
Advanced options
  setting 51
Advanced Options dialog box
  disabling 51
Analysis
  defined 125
ArcGIS license
  changing 43
ArcMap
  starting 8, 16
ArcScan
  enabling 43
    while in an edit session 43
  getting started 32
  in the editing environment 36
  overview 32
  ways of using 32
  working in ArcGIS 32
ArcScan processes
  comparing performances 122
ArcScan toolbar
  adding 44
    with the Tools menu 44
    with the View menu 44
Area
  defined 125
Attribute
  defined 125

B

Background
  defined 125
Band
  defined 125
Batch vectorization 16
  defined 126
  described 2, 32, 87
  overview 88

Brush size
  changing 99
Brush tool
  using 99
Button
  defined 126

C

Cell selection 92
  commands 93
  defined 126
  methods
    expression based 89
    interactive 89
  overview 89
  saving 89
  tools 93
  using with other tools 89
Cell Selection menu 35
Cell size
  defined 126
  described 28
Cell values 29
Cells
  adding 96
  defined 126
  described 28
  erasing 103
Centerline vectorization
  defined 126
  described 34
  of river data 48
Classified rendering option
  setting 46
Classify
  defined 126
Cleanup session 96
  starting 97
  stopping 97

Colors
    filling an area 100
    raster foreground and background
        preset 49, 62
        switching 104
        toggling 49, 62
Column
    defined 126
    of a raster dataset 28
Compression Tolerance
    setting 72, 111
Connected cell area
    finding 93
Connected cell selection
    clearing 95
Connected cells
    diagonal of the envelope
        finding 93
    interactively selecting
        by dragging a box 91
        by single clicking 90
    selecting 33
        using an expression query 92
Continuous surfaces
    examples 29
Control points
    and georeferencing 30
    defined 126
    described 30
Coordinate
    defined 126
Coordinate system
    and raster datasets 30
    defined 126

D

Data
    adding to support vectorization methods 48
Data frames
    defined 127
    editing a map with multiple 42
Data type
    defined 127
Data view
    defined 127
Dataset
    defined 127
Digitizing
    defined 127
Draw tool
    choosing 100

E

Edit cache
    creating 40, 41
    defined 127
    described 40
    toolbar 41
    zooming to extent 41
Edit session
    defined 127
    described 40
    starting 36, 40
    stopping 42
Edit sketch 37
Edit target layer
    changing 13
Edit tasks 37

Editing
    a map with more than one data frame 42
    adding the Editor toolbar 39
    creating an edit cache 41
    in layout view 42
    options
        setting 36
    saving edits 41
    starting 18, 40
    stopping 42
    using the snapping environment 59
    with more than one collection of datasets 40
Editing Options dialog box
    settings 54
Editing tools 38
Editor toolbar
    activating 40
    adding 39
        from the Tools menu 39
        from the View menu 39
        using the Customize dialog box 39
    defined 127
Edits
    saving 38, 55
Ellipse
    defined 127
    drawing 103
Erase tool
    using 103
Erase tool size
    changing 104
Extent
    defined 127

F

Fan Angle
    described 69
    setting 74, 113

Feature class
    defined 128
Features
    defined 127
    generating 24, 88, 117
        inside a defined area 119
        using the centerline vectorization method
            117
        using the outline vectorization method
            118
Field
    defined 128
Fill tool
    using 100
Foreground
    defined 128
Format
    defined 128

G

Gap Closure setting
    disabled 69
    enabled 69
    tolerance 74, 113
Geodatabase
    defined 128
Geometric shapes
    drawing 100
Geometric transformation
    defined 128
    described 30
Georeferencing
    defined 128
    described 30

Grid
    a raster dataset 28
    defined 128

H

Hole size
    setting 75
    specifying 65
Holes
    defined 128
    filling 94
        before tracing 65
    finding in rasters 92

I

Image
    defined 128
Interactive selection method
    changing 90
Interactive selection target
    changing 94
    viewing 94
Interactive vectorization 3
    defined 128
    described 3, 33
Intersection
    described 67
Intersection Solutions
    choosing 109
    Geometrical 67
    Median 67
    None 67

L

Layer
    defined 129
Layer snapping properties
    types
        edge 57
        endpoint 57
        vertex 57
Layout view
    defined 129
    editing in 42
Line features
    creating
        by tracing raster cells 11
        using raster snapping 76
        using the Edit Sketch tool 76
        using the Vectorization Trace tool 80
Line width
    changing 101
    specifying maximum 71, 110
Lines
    drawing 101

M

Magic Erase tool
    using
        by dragging a box 106
        by single clicking 105
Map
    defined 129
Map document
    defined 129
Map projection
    and raster datasets 30
    defined 129
    described 30
Maximum line width
    setting 66

Multiband rasters
    working with 46
Multiple cells
    filling at one time 100
Multiple point lines
    drawing 101

N

NoData
    defined 129
Noise
    defined 129
    removing 96
Null value
    defined 129

O

Optimal performance
    maintaining 51
Optimal settings
    determining 88
Outline vectorization
    defined 129
    described 34
    of river data 48

P

Pixel
    defined 129
Point
    defined 129
Polygon
    defined 129
    drawing 102

Polygon features
    creating 8
        at intersections first 78, 83
        by tracing raster cells 13
        using raster snapping 78
        using the Sketch tool 78
        using the Vectorization Trace tool 83
    generating
        from lines 118
Preview
    updating
        after changing vectorization settings 116
Preview display 2
Preview symbols
    changing 50
    hiding 50
Projection
    defined 130

Q

Query
    defined 130

R

Raster cells
    described 28
    ignoring during tracing 81, 84
    tracing 33
Raster centerlines
    snapping to 3
Raster Cleanup
    defined 130
    described 5, 18
    edits
        saving 97
    using cell selection tools 20
Raster Cleanup commands
    using 107

Raster Cleanup menu 35
Raster Cleanup session 97
Raster data
    cleaning up 33
    preparing
        for vectorization 96
Raster dataset
    and coordinate space 30
    defined 130
    georeferencing 30
    understanding 28
Raster edits
    saving 96, 108
        to a new file 108
Raster intersection
    defined 130
Raster intersections
    snapping to 3
Raster layer symbology
    changing 8, 16, 45
Raster layers
    symbolizing 32
Raster line width
    determining 63, 66
    specifying the maximum 63
Raster Line Width tool 35, 68
    using 66
Raster lines
    containing holes 65
Raster Painting toolbar 35
    opening 98
Raster Painting tools
    using 99
Raster postprocessing
    defined 130
Raster preprocessing 88
    defined 130
    described 1, 34, 88
Raster selection 4
    saving
        to a new file 95

Styles
    defined 132
    described 2
Symbol
    defined 132
Symbology
    defined 132

T

Table
    defined 132
Table of contents
    defined 132
Target layer 37, 54
    defined 132
Target raster layer
    selecting 47
Tolerance
    defined 132
Topology 38
    defined 133

U

Undo command 38

V

Values
    of raster cells 29
Vector
    defined 133
Vectorization
    defined 133
    described 32
    previewing 23, 116
Vectorization menu 35

Vectorization method
    centerline 48
    changing 48, 117
    outline 48
Vectorization options
    setting 48
Vectorization settings 55
    applying
        for batch vectorization 109
        for raster tracing 71
    compression tolerance 68
    defined 133
    fan angle 69
    gap closure tolerance 69
    holes 70
    intersection solution 67
    maximum line width 68
    overview 67
    retaining 115
    smoothing weight 69
    styles 70
    using 22
Vectorization Settings dialog box 2, 67
    modeless 71, 109
Vectorization style
    loading 115
    saving 114
Vectorization Trace tool 35
    defined 133
    using 55
Vectorization Trace tool versus Sketch tool 55
Vertex
    defined 133
Vertices
    changing the maximum number in a polygon
        118

W

Workspaces
    defined 133
    editing a map with multiple 40